20 EXCITING PLAYS
FOR
MEDIEVAL HISTORY
CLASSES

DEAN R. BOWMAN

J. WESTON
WALCH
PUBLISHER

PORTLAND, MAINE

User's Guide
to
Walch Reproducible Books

As part of our general effort to provide educational materials which are as practical and economical as possible, we have designated this publication a "reproducible book." The designation means that purchase of the book includes purchase of the right to limited reproduction of all pages on which this symbol appears:

Here is the basic Walch policy: We grant to individual purchasers of this book the right to make sufficient copies of reproducible pages for use by all students of a single teacher. This permission is limited to a single teacher, and does not apply to entire schools or school systems, so institutions purchasing the book should pass the permission on to a single teacher. Copying of the book or its parts for resale is prohibited.

Any questions regarding this policy or requests to purchase further reproduction rights should be addressed to:

Permissions Editor
J. Weston Walch, Publisher
321 Valley Street • P. O. Box 658
Portland, Maine 04104-0658

On the cover: Sailors using an astrolabe to find their latitude at sea; adapted from an early fourteenth century French manuscript, Livre des Merveilles.

1   2   3   4   5   6   7   8   9   10
ISBN 0-8251-2164-7
Copyright © 1992
J. Weston Walch, Publisher
P. O. Box 658 • Portland, Maine 04104-0658
Printed in the United States of America

Contents

To the Teacher v

The Plays

*Choral parts

To the Teacher

These plays are designed to involve as many student readers as possible. Over half of the plays have a Greek-style chorus as part of the cast of characters; the chorus is designed to fill in historical details, and at the same time include more students in the reading or performance. Each chorus has up to four speaking parts: I, II, III, and IV. You may choose to use a four-voice chorus, or instead use an even larger chorus, casting several students as Voice I, several others as Voice II, and so on. This method has two advantages: It involves many students (the entire class, if you wish), and it creates a more powerful choral effect.

Still, many students are disappointed when they are not chosen for the "big" roles. To involve the most students in the major roles, consider dividing the class into four groups, one for each corner of the room. Have each group select roles and then read the play aloud. This method wouldn't work well in a small room, and even in a larger room it might sound a little too lively to have so many students reading at once. But this method does have the advantage of involving every student in the class. It also gives more of them a chance to practice reading the text. In the next class session, the play can be read in a more conventional way.

No matter how you choose to use these plays—as simple oral readings or full, costumed productions—they will enliven the people and events of medieval history in a way that will delight both you and your students.

Justinian and Theodora:
The Byzantine Golden Age

Characters

CHORUS I, II, III, IV
THEODORA, carnival actress,
  future empress
MAX, aide to Justinian
JUSTINIAN, emperor of Byzantine
  Empire

TRIBONIAN, legal scholar
BELISARIUS, army leader
MENAS, high Orthodox
  church official

Prologue

CHORUS:

I:	Rome, Rome, complete now your decay,
II:	An Empire withering in the West;
III:	While in the East resumes your proud sway
IV:	For a thousand years under Byzantine's crest.
I:	Justinian, the illiterate peasant's son,
II:	Would mount Byzantium's grand throne
III:	And return to her what long ago was won
IV:	By the great and glorious empire of Rome.
I:	A passion for unity consumed his soul,
II:	So the legal system was revised;
III:	Making it logical was the goal,
IV:	Bringing order, so highly prized.
I:	His armies regained many lost lands
II:	To the North and to the West;
III:	His capital, destroyed by riotous bands,
IV:	Rebuilt, became his legacy seen best.

I:	Behind his vision and greatness,
II:	And often leading him, too:
III:	His wife, Theodora, the empress,
IV:	Supporter, defender, and inspiration new.

Scene I: Market area, Constantinople, c. A.D. 524.

THEODORA:	You wish to buy some wool? What are you eyeing so closely?
MAX:	You.
THEODORA:	Me? I'm not for sale.
MAX:	Theodora...come, come now.
THEODORA:	How do you know my name? What do you want?
MAX:	My master wants to know you better.
THEODORA:	Then he should have come himself!
MAX:	Snippy, snippy.... Would you expect the nephew of the emperor to come down here?
THEODORA:	Why not? Emperors, slaves, merchants, and midwives... we're all the same.
MAX:	Even the daughter of a circus bear tamer...who later becomes a prostitute?
THEODORA:	Lies! I'm just a poor, honest working woman.
MAX:	Maybe...but I've done some investigating....
THEODORA:	Tell your master that cowards and liars love dealing with the past. Only the brave and noble do battle with the present.
MAX:	I understand how Justinian, my master, was captivated by your great beauty. But I don't think you two are compatible.
THEODORA:	And why is that? What are his interests?

MAX:	Many—architecture, law, music, philosophy, poetry, theology....
THEODORA:	And you think I'm too simple and narrow?
MAX:	No. It's your lifestyles that are so different.
THEODORA:	What are you talking about?
MAX:	Justinian is very religious, very devout. He lives like a monk ...eating and sleeping very little. He's always working! You, I've learned, enjoy eating, sleeping, and drinking to excess. What life could you two possibly share?
THEODORA:	A royal one.

Scene II: Justinian's home, Constantinople, A.D. 527.

THEODORA:	Mistress...wife...and now empress. What more could happen?
JUSTINIAN:	You rule with me.
THEODORA:	Preposterous! I have no authority.
JUSTINIAN:	You will. Remember, I am the emperor, divinely appointed to rule this Empire, restore its lost lands, safeguard and spread the Christian faith.
THEODORA:	How can I help you?
JUSTINIAN:	Tell me how I can be a better emperor.
THEODORA:	I know what it's like to be poor and needy. Protect them, and promote their welfare.
JUSTINIAN:	Yes...go on....
THEODORA:	Provide work for the unemployed.
JUSTINIAN:	Yes, in the state bakeries and gardens.
THEODORA:	Build more special-care facilities for the orphans, the sick, the handicapped, and the aged.

JUSTINIAN:	That's in the true Christian spirit. But the public treasury is not bottomless, and you know how people feel about increased taxes.
THEODORA:	Then prod, push, and encourage the wealthy to endow hospitals and orphanages with their own money! Remind them of their Christian duty.
JUSTINIAN:	Anything else?
THEODORA:	Women! They need greater rights and protection... and the slaves need these things as well.

Scene III: Imperial palace, Constantinople, A.D. 527.

TRIBONIAN:	Yes, emperor....
JUSTINIAN:	Tribonian, you are considered the finest legal mind in the Empire. Therefore, you must realize what a mess our legal system has become.
TRIBONIAN:	I do. It's a disorganized mish-mash. Some laws contradict each other, too many are out of date.... In fact, there are far too many laws!
JUSTINIAN:	And this chaos only confuses judges and average citizens alike... breeding contempt and disrespect for all laws.
TRIBONIAN:	I suppose you want me to codify the whole mess.
JUSTINIAN:	Yes. Make it logical, consistent, and simple enough for all to understand.
TRIBONIAN:	I'll need time and expert help.
JUSTINIAN:	You have my authority.
TRIBONIAN:	There will be much pruning. Any guidelines?
JUSTINIAN:	The average citizen must be protected.
TRIBONIAN:	Like the right to be safe in your own home, and the right to a speedy trial?

JUSTINIAN:	Yes. And reasonable loan rates for borrowers. Builders are to be responsible for faulty construction. They must pay for any needed repairs. And . . . no one has the right to store noxious or hazardous materials where others live nearby.
TRIBONIAN:	Anything about punishment?
JUSTINIAN:	It must always take into account the age and circumstances of the offender.
TRIBONIAN:	How about a violent crime, like rape?
JUSTINIAN:	The death penalty.
TRIBONIAN:	Even if the victim is a slave woman?
JUSTINIAN:	Most certainly! All women must be protected.
TRIBONIAN:	What about adultery?
JUSTINIAN:	Do you know what caused Rome to decay and finally rot? Not invading barbarians! It was sexual immorality and moral chaos. They became animals! The family structure that held the nation together broke down.
TRIBONIAN:	The death penalty for adultery, then?
JUSTINIAN:	The safeguarding of order throughout the Empire begins in the marriage. I hate chaos, because it's like an incurable disease. Adultery is a form of chaos, and marriage must not be contaminated by it!

CHORUS:

I:	Logically organized and codified,
II:	Justinian's system became
III:	A beacon of justice far and wide,
IV:	And a legacy greater than his fame.
I:	But Byzantine law stirred no passions;
II:	Like horses racing in the hippodrome new,
III:	The crowds split into colored factions:
IV:	The commoners green and the wealthy blue.

20 Exciting Plays for Medieval History Classes

I:	Each side would cheer its favorite rider,
II:	Wearing of course its colors true,
III:	But often the action spread far wider
IV:	Than the sport each came to view.

I:	For on the mount of every horse
II:	Rode the politics of its backers,
III:	And the victors could set the course
IV:	Of some important civic matters.

I:	So Greens and Blues fought and died
II:	In the stadium and the street,
III:	Their political power all but nullified
IV:	Until the day their goals did meet.

Scene IV: Imperial palace, A.D. 532.

MAX:	Emperor, the revolt is growing dangerously!
JUSTINIAN:	I'm sure the different colored factions will soon tire each other out, and it will end.
MAX:	No, no, you are mistaken! The Blues and Greens have joined forces! They are rampaging all over the city yelling "*Nika! Nika!*"
JUSTINIAN:	They're yelling "Victory!"? Do they really think they've won?
MAX:	They control the streets, burning at random.
JUSTINIAN:	Theodora, we must escape to our country villa!
THEODORA:	No! Don't cower from them! You are the emperor!
JUSTINIAN:	The government? The bureaucracy? Are they still loyal to me?
MAX:	Senator Hypatius has been persuaded to assume the throne.
JUSTINIAN:	But I thought Hypatius was—

THEODORA: Don't think. Act! Call for Belisarius. And stay here, on your throne, like an emperor!

Scene V: Hours later.

BELISARIUS: The revolt is ended. Your imperial control is now absolute.

JUSTINIAN: It started in the hippodrome, right? All those screaming people watching the races and thinking they could scream at me! What happened?

BELISARIUS: We entered the hippodrome, and in a few hours left over thirty thousand of the traitors dead.

THEODORA: The rest of the city?

BELISARIUS: Calm now . . . but most of it has burned down, even the Church of St. Sophia.

JUSTINIAN: No matter what the cost, this city will be rebuilt. Constantinople will be more beautiful and grand than before. And the crown jewel will be a new St. Sophia.

BELISARIUS: My orders, Emperor?

JUSTINIAN: Reclaim the Empire's lost lands in North Africa, Italy, and Spain. Throw back the barbarians!

Scene VI: Outside the new St. Sophia Church (Hagia Sophia), Constantinople, December 26, A.D. 537.

THEODORA: Justinian, my dear, your crowning achievement awaits its dedication. You must feel on top of the world.

JUSTINIAN: Well . . . yes.

THEODORA: Why do you seem a bit downcast?

JUSTINIAN: The people hate me.

THEODORA: But you have done so much for them! Is there any city on earth more grand than ours? *You* are its architect and builder.

20 Exciting Plays for Medieval History Classes

JUSTINIAN: But the cost. . . .

THEODORA: Imperial armies have restored many lands to the Empire.

JUSTINIAN: But the cost, Theodora! I emptied the treasury and raised taxes.

THEODORA: So what! Everyone complains about taxes. Look, my dear, look beyond the petty gripes of the people to the soaring dome of the Hagia Sophia. You built it! Doesn't that lift your spirits?

JUSTINIAN: Yes . . . no activity has given me greater joy than the hours spent working on the church.

(Group enters church for dedication.)

MENAS: The dome! It looks as if it reaches the very heavens! Glory to the Almighty!

MAX: How did the architects do it? The dome seems to float like a fixed cloud. What supports it?

MENAS: Never have I seen such beautiful and inspiring mosaics! The colors are dazzling!

MAX: *(counting)* Thirty-eight, thirty-nine . . . *forty* silver chandeliers!

MENAS: All this was done in less than six years? A miracle!

THEODORA: King Solomon had his great temple in Jerusalem, but you, my husband—

JUSTINIAN: Yes . . . truly, I have outdone even him.

20 Exciting Plays for Medieval History Classes

Epilogue: The Byzantine Empire

CHORUS:

I:	Preserver of Greek and Roman light,
II:	Brave dike against barbarism's fierce tide,
III:	Bastion of Orthodox Christian might,
IV:	Bringer of Russia to Europe's side.
I:	But the rising flood of Islam
II:	Did lap, then crash, Constantinople's door,
III:	Leaving a heart to draw upon
IV:	Only the blood of her religious core.
I:	Far from the Renaissance, and Reformation, too,
II:	Your culture was caught in a static grip;
III:	Fearful of change, and most things new,
IV:	Your children await, the mind-chains to slip.

Prince Shotoku (A.D. 574–622), Founder of Japanese Civilization

---

Characters

OTOBOI, YASI, ARATA, court
  officials
SHOTOKU, prince and regent
HYEJA, Buddhist teacher

HAKKA, Confucian scholar
  and teacher
SUIKO, empress

Scene I: Imperial court, Japan, c. A.D. 552.

OTOBOI: Have you seen the gifts a Korean king sent to our emperor?

YASI: The Buddhist images and scriptures?

OTOBOI: Yes. What do you think?

YASI: You know I'm not very religious. I don't see what significance Buddhism can have here in Japan.

OTOBOI: Maybe you don't, but the court is buzzing like bees about it.

YASI: For a foreign religion? How absurd! The next thing you know they'll want to import the rest of Chinese culture.

OTOBOI: You might be right.... There are some powerful people in the court who are very attracted to Buddhism and Chinese civilization.

YASI: Why? What's the point? Personally, I think we all should be content with our own ways . . . and keep out alien ones!

OTOBOI: I don't think that's possible.

YASI: Why not? A wide sea separates us from the continent.

OTOBOI:	You can't keep life from changing…at least for very long. Being a group of islands is most fortunate for us. We can more clearly see what changes are coming.
YASI:	And that gives us the chance to pick and choose more wisely, correct?
OTOBOI:	Correct, my friend.

Scene II: Imperial court, Japan, c. A.D. 586.

ARATA:	Are you ready for your lessons?
SHOTOKU:	Yes. Are both teachers nearby?
ARATA:	They are. Which tutor would you like to see first, the Buddhist or the Confucian?
SHOTOKU:	Send them both in.
ARATA:	Most unusual. I don't think you've ever met with them together. Any reason?
SHOTOKU:	I'm just thinking into the future….
ARATA:	When you are emperor?
SHOTOKU:	I doubt that will ever happen. But I might someday be in a position of considerable influence.
	(Enter HYEJA and HAKKA.)
HYEJA:	You wish a session with both of us?
HAKKA:	This could be confusing. What is your purpose?
SHOTOKU:	To *learn*, my esteemed masters, to *learn*!
HYEJA:	We are at your service.
SHOTOKU:	Tell me…how can Buddhism benefit Japan?
HYEJA:	You are a devout follower. Why do you ask me?

SHOTOKU:	Because I can only answer for myself what Buddhism means. You've seen what it can mean for a whole people.
HYEJA:	You are right. Buddhism can instill in the people all the virtues of good citizenship.
SHOTOKU:	For instance?
HYEJA:	Peacefulness, obedience, goodness, the security and comfort of shared values . . . unity.
SHOTOKU:	Unity. . . . Do you really believe Buddhism can help unify all the peoples of our sacred islands?
HYEJA:	Most certainly. But it will take time, energy, resources . . . and, above all, the commitment of our leaders.
SHOTOKU:	What does Confucianism offer to building a nation?
HAKKA:	The essential principles of order and merit.
SHOTOKU:	Meaning what?
HAKKA:	Without well-ordered individuals, there are no well-ordered families—
SHOTOKU:	And that leads to chaos in communities and the nation.
HAKKA:	Just as Confucius taught. You've learned well.
SHOTOKU:	What did he teach about merit?
HAKKA:	That the power and position of government officials should not be based on family ties—
SHOTOKU:	—but on individual merit and qualifications, right?
HAKKA:	Right. Confucius wanted all, rich and poor, to have the same opportunity to take the government entrance tests.
SHOTOKU:	Thank you both. This has been most informative.
	(Exit SHOTOKU.)
HAKKA:	For a twelve-year-old he certainly asks a lot of questions.
HYEJA:	He's certainly bright . . . I wonder where he's headed?

Scene III: Imperial court, Japan, c. A.D. 593.

ARATA: The empress wishes to speak with you.

SHOTOKU: I am her willing servant.

(They enter Empress SUIKO's presence.)

SUIKO: Good morning, Nephew. How does it feel to be a prince?

SHOTOKU: How does it feel to be the new empress?

SUIKO: Very heavy. That's why I called for you.

SHOTOKU: What is your desire, dear Aunt?

SUIKO: To delegate all my imperial authority to you. Though you're just twenty, I want you to rule as regent.

SHOTOKU: I am more than willing...but why are you doing this?

SUIKO: I have no stomach for affairs of state. Look what happened to the last emperor...assassinated over a petty feud with the Soga clan. I want to protect the imperial family's safety.

SHOTOKU: I appreciate your confidence in me.

SUIKO: You are very intelligent and virtuous, Nephew.

SHOTOKU: You are most kind and generous, Aunt.

SUIKO: And I believe you sincerely seek the best for all our people.

SHOTOKU: That is how I have been raised since birth.

SUIKO: Tell me, dear Nephew, what you intend to do with this power and authority.

SHOTOKU: First, I'm going to do everything I can to promote and spread Buddhism.

SUIKO: Because it will help bring about social harmony?

SHOTOKU: Yes, and a spirit of hope for our poorest classes.

SUIKO: How will you go about this?

SHOTOKU: By building temples, financing teachers, and enacting citizen codes of behavior based on Buddhism.

SUIKO: Will you encourage other foreign ideas?

SHOTOKU: Indeed I will. I'm going to encourage Chinese scholars and artisans to come to Japan.

SUIKO: And will you send our people across the sea?

SHOTOKU: To learn? Of course. Where better to learn Chinese civilization?

SUIKO: What other great changes do you intend?

SHOTOKU: Limiting the powers of the great families.

SUIKO: That will not be easy.

SHOTOKU: But it must be done! Our officials should not be ranked by social and family connections, but by individual merit.

SUIKO: How can you do that? Old ways die hard...and very slowly....

SHOTOKU: By creating a twelve-cap ranking system for officials, a system that recognizes and rewards talent above all other concerns.

SUIKO: And not a fixed system based on family background?

SHOTOKU: No. We cannot progress with the old ways.

SUIKO: You truly seek to build a new nation, don't you?

SHOTOKU: Yes, one moving forward, with our emperor as the great unifier of all classes.

Muhammad and the Rise of Islam

Characters

CHORUS I, II, III, IV
KHADIJA, Muhammad's wife
MUHAMMAD
ZAID, Muhammad's servant and follower
ABU BAKR, follower of Islam

OMAR, follower of Islam
AISHA, follower of Islam in Medina
TORK, citizen of Medina
LAUD, follower of Islam in Medina

Prologue

CHORUS:

I:	When the grandeur of Imperial Rome
II:	Was a sinking memory in the West,
III:	Far away Arabia was the home
IV:	Of tribal warfare without rest.
I:	Each tribe had its very own idol,
II:	And, of course, a particular cause,
III:	Ever fighting for survival,
IV:	Unrestrained by common laws.
I:	Yet all the while rich caravans
II:	From beyond brought ideas and trade,
III:	Crossing over the burning sands,
IV:	Stopping only for rest and shade.
I:	And in one dry valley city,
II:	Aye, the gathering place named Mecca,
III:	There was housed each tribal deity,
IV:	In a sanctuary called the Kaaba.

I:	There in the sixth century, A.D.,
II:	Was born a man who'd bring
III:	To Arabs a dynamic unity
IV:	In a religion all-encompassing.

I:	Orphaned at an early age,
II:	With grandfather and uncle as his guides,
III:	He earned in transport his living wage,
IV:	Traveling far on caravan rides.

I:	At twenty-five he married,
II:	And became a prosperous man;
III:	Yet in his soul he carried
IV:	Mysteries hard to understand.

I:	Mysteries of voices and visions
II:	Made clear a new spiritual plan:
III:	Islam, he called the religion,
IV:	Revealed in his words: the Koran.

Scene I: Mecca, Arabia, c. A.D. 610.

KHADIJA:	Dear husband, you seem troubled lately. Is there something wrong with the business?
MUHAMMAD:	No. The caravan trade goes well.
KHADIJA:	Are you ill, then?
MUHAMMAD:	No...I've had some very unusual experiences...and they frighten me.
KHADIJA:	When you go out to meditate on Mt. Hira?
MUHAMMAD:	Yes.
KHADIJA:	Tell me what happened...please! It grieves me to see you so anxious and unsettled.

MUHAMMAD:	I've been afraid to tell you. While resting in a cave I've had visions and heard voices...I cannot tell you more...I'm afraid you will laugh, or think your husband has lost his mind.
KHADIJA:	You know me better than that. Trust me, confide in me. You are a good and noble man, respected by all, one who can only speak the truth.
MUHAMMAD:	The Angel Gabriel came and told me to recite.
KHADIJA:	Recite what?
MUHAMMAD:	That there is no god but Allah, and I, Muhammad, am his last messenger.
KHADIJA:	What is the message?
MUHAMMAD:	What I just told you—all the tribal idols are crude creations of man. There is no god but Allah.
KHADIJA:	The Jews and Christians believe in only one god.
MUHAMMAD:	Yes...they are people of the Book. But they have corrupted and complicated their original beliefs.
KHADIJA:	What are you going to do?
MUHAMMAD:	Khadija, do you believe that Allah has chosen me to be his final messenger on earth?
KHADIJA:	Yes.
MUHAMMAD:	Then I will share this revelation with my close friends and family.
KHADIJA:	Share it beyond them, to all Arabia.
MUHAMMAD:	To all the Arab tribes?
KHADIJA:	Yes! Bring them together under your words. Unite the separate tribes into a great and glorious nation!
MUHAMMAD:	As Allah wills it....

20 Exciting Plays for Medieval History Classes

Scene II: Mecca, Arabia, early September, A.D. 622.

ZAID:	I'm very worried about the prophet's safety.
ABU BAKR:	I, as well.
OMAR:	Once he began preaching so aggressively in public, his enemies in the Quraysh clan organized.
ZAID:	They're all afraid.
ABU BAKR:	Afraid Muhammad's teaching about only one god will end their profitable trade.
OMAR:	The disgusting trade in idols and false pilgrimages to the Kaaba.
ZAID:	Those pilgrimages have become nothing more than a disgraceful carnival, an offense to all true Muslims.
ABU BAKR:	But a very profitable carnival, nonetheless.
OMAR:	The Quraysh are worried also about losing their political power. They despise Muhammad's teaching that we're all the same before Allah: merchant and slave, light-skinned and dark.
ABU BAKR:	Remember the slaves who became followers of Muhammad? The city leaders treated them terribly!
OMAR:	Shamelessly trying to get them to renounce Islam by putting them in jail. . . .
ZAID:	Or out in the burning sun with no protection.
ABU BAKR:	That's why I purchased those slaves' freedom!
OMAR:	Let's face it . . . the Quraysh want Muhammad dead before his message spreads any further.
ABU BAKR:	That's why we must act immediately to save him.
ZAID:	You mean fight?
ABU BAKR:	Not now . . . they are too strong.

OMAR:	Flee? To where? Remember how Muhammad was treated in Taif. He was rejected and pelted with rocks. Where would he be safe to preach his message?
ABU BAKR:	Medina. Many merchants from that city already know him and his message. They are sympathetic to Islam, and will welcome and protect Muhammad.
ZAID:	But will Muhammad be willing to leave Mecca? This is his home. You know nothing is more important to an Arab than his family and clan.
OMAR:	Of course . . . but Muhammad believes that his message is more important than blood ties. Besides, he wants us all to unite under Islam.
ZAID:	If he gains more followers in Medina, maybe he'll someday be able to return safely to Mecca.
ABU BAKR:	Yes, and in triumph! But first we must be patient, and make sure he flees before Abu Sufyan and his men can do him harm.

Scene III: Marketplace, Medina, Arabia, c. A.D. 624.

AISHA:	Welcome home, Tork. How long have you been away from Medina?
TORK:	Two years on a caravan to the Far East.
LAUD:	Then you will find many good changes.
TORK:	What? You must be joking. Nothing changes in Arabia but the weather. It's always the same: tribes feuding and fighting, a truce, and then more feuding and fighting.
AISHA:	Not any more. Many Arabs are now united.
TORK:	Again you are joking! Arabs are united only in death; while they live, they fight each other.
LAUD:	Muhammad, our leader, has united all the warring tribes of Medina.
TORK:	Muhammad? Who's he?

AISHA:	Allah's messenger.
TORK:	Come on, now . . . in India I saw hundreds of so-called prophets and holy men. What makes Muhammad different?
LAUD:	He speaks clearly and with great authority.
AISHA:	No one can fail to understand his message.
TORK:	What is it?
LAUD:	All people are the same before Allah.
AISHA:	All are to submit completely to Allah's will.
TORK:	And what *is* Allah's will?
LAUD:	Islam has five pillars for all Muslims to uphold.
AISHA:	First, faith in Allah, and belief in Muhammad as his last messenger.
LAUD:	Second, prayer five times a day, facing Mecca.
AISHA:	Third, complete fasting during the daylight hours of the month of Ramadan.
LAUD:	Fourth, giving alms money to the poor and for the building of mosques—our houses of prayer.
AISHA:	And finally, if possible, a pilgrimage to Mecca.
TORK:	Just those five things? Nothing more?
LAUD:	There is much, much more, concerning how we are to live, conduct business, govern, live with others. . . .
TORK:	For example?
AISHA:	We are to be a sober people whose behavior pleases Allah.
TORK:	Meaning?
AISHA:	We are not to drink alcohol or gamble.
LAUD:	Our women are to have legal rights and property rights.

AISHA:	We are to be fair and just to all people who respect Islam, even non-Muslims.
TORK:	How do you know these things?
AISHA:	They are the words of Muhammad, our leader.
LAUD:	Words that we believe Allah has spoken directly to him.
AISHA:	Come with us to hear Muhammad.
LAUD:	And then you'll understand why we follow him.
AISHA:	And why so many of the tribes are putting aside their differences to unit under Islam.
TORK:	Yes . . . I would like very much to meet this extraordinary man.

Epilogue

CHORUS:

I:	Like a mighty wind, Islam gathered
II:	The many tribes of Arabia,
III:	Building a force that shattered
IV:	Centuries of weakness and inertia.
I:	Islam was the new faith,
II:	Muhammad, Allah's messenger,
III:	Sweeping across lands in a lightning swath,
IV:	Bringing in millions beneath its banner.
I:	From the spice islands of Indonesia
II:	To the irrigated plains of Moorish Spain,
III:	Down through the heart of Africa,
IV:	Muhammad's legacy would reign.

20 Exciting Plays for Medieval History Classes

The Battle of Tours, A.D. 732

Characters

LEO, Christian monk   **GAMEL**, Saracen sword maker
GILLE, Frankish army cook   **RAHMAN**, Saracen leader
AKAR, Saracen soldier   **ABD**, aide to Rahman
IMAD, Saracen scholar   **CHARLES**, mayor of the palace
OMAR, Saracen horse trainer   **REN**, aide to Charles

Scene I: Countryside near Tours, France, October, A.D. 732.

LEO: Pax vobiscum.

GILLE: What?

LEO: It's a greeting of peace. I'm a priest, my son. Where are you going?

GILLE: To Lord Raymonde's for foodstuffs. I am a cook in Charles's army.

LEO: May I accompany you? I need to see Lord Raymonde myself. I'll show the way.

GILLE: Thank you. Is it far?

LEO: No. It's just beyond those trees ahead. . . .

GILLE: Priest! Those men running towards us don't look like Franks! Excuse me, but I'm off. . . .

(Enter AKAR, IMAD, OMAR, and GAMEL.)

AKAR: Guards! Take these fat-bellied infidels to the stables.

GILLE: Priest! Do something! We've stumbled into the Saracens' camp! They'll slaughter us like pigs.

LEO:	Ah...salaam!
IMAD:	Pax vobiscum.
LEO:	Et cum spiritu tuo.
GILLE:	There you go again. What's happening?
LEO:	A good sign. This Saracen knows Latin.
IMAD:	And Greek, and Arabic. Don't be afraid. We Saracens are quite civilized. Besides, as followers of the prophet Muhammad, we are forbidden to eat pork! Ha!
GILLE:	Where is Lord Raymonde?
AKAR:	The sight of our fleet horses approaching, I believe, sent him to the Franks' camp.
GILLE:	In that case, allow me to do likewise. I'm just a simple cook....
AKAR:	A cook? Excellent. You can be most useful. Come with me.

(AKAR and GILLE exit.)

LEO:	I doubt I can be as useful as Gille, unless you wish to learn about the Christian faith, and our Frankish culture.
IMAD:	I know about your religion, and I respect it. But we Muslims cannot accept the divinity of Jesus. A prophet, yes, but Muhammad is Allah's last and greatest. As for your Frankish culture, compared to ours, it's a zero.
LEO:	Zero? What does that mean? I've never heard the word before.
IMAD:	Just as I thought. You heirs of the great Roman Empire know nothing of mathematics. Your number system is crude and clumsy; ours is ingenious and infinitely practical. Your so-called culture is doomed.
LEO:	What? You think Saracen math will conquer Frankish warriors protecting their own land?
IMAD:	I don't think you realize what you are up against.
LEO:	I'm listening.

20 Exciting Plays for Medieval History Classes

IMAD:	A little more than a hundred years ago Muhammad united all the warring tribes of Arabia. Under the banner of Islam, we Arabs conquered Persia, and reached the very walls of Constantinople. Then, we swept across North Africa to Spain. The rest of Christian Europe will soon fall to us as well.
LEO:	You have only conquered weak and divided peoples. Charles will stem the Saracen tide.
IMAD:	Follow me, please. Fifteen years ago, at Constantinople, Emperor Leo poured hot tar and burning oil on our heads. But today there are no walls to climb; we face the enemy across a long, flat plain. Omar, tell our visitor about your beauties from Arabia.
LEO:	You think pretty women will distract our men?
OMAR:	Imad is referring to our beautiful horses! No finer horse exists than our Arabians, fast as the wind, more fierce than the desert sun.
IMAD:	I know for a fact that your Charles has no cavalry.
LEO:	But his men are better armed than yours. Saracen soldiers will fall from their horses like ripe apples.
IMAD:	Gamel, bring us some of your swords.
GAMEL:	We Arabs make the finest steel in the world. Look . . . this blade can be bent double and still not break.
IMAD:	Watch closely.
GAMEL:	*(brandishing the sword)* A blade so sharp it can cut through the finest hair, even a Christian's! *(He cuts a lock of LEO's hair.)* WHOOSH! Or infidel steel bars . . . BWANG! We call it a Damascus blade.
LEO:	I see. Thanks for the haircut.
IMAD:	Now, good priest, would you like to learn about Islam? Your churches will soon be replaced by our mosques.
OMAR:	He doesn't look convinced. Gamel, tell him why our soldiers fight so bravely.
GAMEL:	For warriors of Islam, death in battle brings immediate entrance to Paradise. Muhammad so promised.

© 1992 J. Weston Walch, Publisher   *20 Exciting Plays for Medieval History Classes*

IMAD: So you see, good priest, time is running out for Christian Europe. Our leader, Abd-al-Rahman, readies for the decisive battle. After our victory we'll teach you Arabic so you can read the Koran.

Scene II: Saracen camp, near Tours, one week later.

RAHMAN: How fare the troops?

ABD: They grow restless. For seven days and seven nights we have sat still before the Franks' camp. We are losing our advantage with each passing hour.

RAHMAN: You are right. The time has come. Gather the troops.

ABD: Immediately, sire.

RAHMAN: Men of Islam, we fight for our faith. Death wings you to Paradise. Victory brings the riches of Europe. Mount your horses... Allah be with you!

Scene III: Frankish camp, near Tours, same time.

CHARLES: When will those Saracens ever move?

(REN comes rushing in.)

REN: The Saracens have mounted! I barely escaped!

CHARLES: Into your formations, men! Shoulder to shoulder! Stay together! Don't break ranks!

Scene IV: Lord Raymonde's stables, late the next day.

(Enter OMAR and IMAD.)

LEO: How did the great battle go?

IMAD: For your people, victory. Our leader is dead.

GILLE: I thought your cavalry was invincible.

OMAR: The Franks would not break. They stood like ice blocks in a box. My horses broke instead.

LEO: What now for your survivors?

IMAD: Retreat across the Pyrenees to Spain. There we are well fortified.

LEO: And your vision of mosques strung across Europe?

IMAD: It was not Allah's will. It is time to build on what we already have.

GILLE: What happened to Charles? Did he survive?

OMAR: Yes. His men kept yelling, "Martel! Martel!" What does that mean?

GILLE: In our language, "martel" means "hammer."

OMAR: Of course. Never have I seen a warrior strike such blows!

LEO: From this day forth he's sure to be called "Charles Martel." I wonder if he realizes what his victory means?

20 Exciting Plays for Medieval History Classes

Charlemagne (A.D. 742–814), First Holy Roman Emperor

<table>
<tr><td colspan="2">Characters</td></tr>
<tr><td>CHORUS I, II, III, IV</td><td>OMNRAD and BOKOR,
Frankish nobles</td></tr>
<tr><td>BERTRADA, Charlemagne's
mother</td><td>EINHARD, scholar, aide to
Charlemagne</td></tr>
<tr><td>CHARLES (Charlemagne)</td><td>ALCUIN, teacher from England</td></tr>
<tr><td>FULRAD, tutor</td><td>DUNGAL and CLEMENT, Irish
monks and teachers</td></tr>
<tr><td>PEPIN, king of the Franks
and Charlemagne's father</td><td></td></tr>
</table>

Prologue

CHORUS:

I:	Imperial Rome, in pathetic stages,
II:	In the West decayed, then finally fell;
III:	In its debris began the Dark Ages,
IV:	A dimly lit retreat towards hell.
I:	Law and order were cast adrift,
II:	Fear was a person's daily bread.
III:	Might was right, and vengeance swift;
IV:	Peace only visited the dead.
I:	But one dim light kept burning
II:	As progress seemed left in the lurch.
III:	A refuge of hope and learning—
IV:	The Roman Catholic Church.
I:	Kings were weak and dissolute,
II:	Disunity, the norm of the day;

III:	Only the Church seemed resolute
IV:	In keeping barbarism at bay.
I:	But a new threat to Western Europe
II:	Arose from Islamic Spain:
III:	Warriors of Arabia's Prophet,
IV:	Seeking this continent to gain.
I:	Who could stem this Saracen tide,
II:	From drowning the Christian bell?
III:	Leading the dauntless Frankish side,
IV:	The mighty hammer: Charles Martel.
I:	At Tours, in present-day France,
II:	The Islamic wave would crest,
III:	And leave behind its best chance
IV:	Of submerging the Christian West.
I:	With the victory a dynasty was won,
II:	Where order and unity might reign;
III:	First Martel, then Pepin his son,
IV:	And then the strongest: Charlemagne.

Scene I: Palace, Ponthion, Frankland, c. A.D. 754.

BERTRADA:	Charles! You're all wet!
CHARLES:	Of course I am, mother. I've been out for my early morning swim.
BERTRADA:	Dry off quickly or you'll be late for your lessons.
CHARLES:	Mother, have I ever kept Abbé Fulrad waiting?
	(Enter FULRAD.)
FULRAD:	I can answer that . . . never.

BERTRADA:	It just seems that Charles spends too much time swimming, hunting, wrestling, and riding.
FULRAD:	Twelve-year-old boys have lots of energy. Besides, such activities are excellent preparation for a future king.
BERTRADA:	Are you his teacher or his coach? I'm concerned about his lessons, especially religious studies.
FULRAD:	Don't fret. Charles shows the same enthusiasm and energy for learning as he does for play. And...he loves the Church.
CHARLES:	When I'm king I will devote all my energies to spreading the Christian faith.
BERTRADA:	God give you the strength! Our Saxon neighbors will fight you tooth and nail. They hate everything our faith and civilization stand for.
FULRAD:	They've slaughtered our missionaries, and burned our churches in their raids.
CHARLES:	I'll make them change their ways!
FULRAD:	You'll need the patience of Job and skills of Joshua!
	(Enter PEPIN.)
PEPIN:	How are the lessons going?
FULRAD:	Very well. We're discussing how to best handle the Saxon barbarians.
PEPIN:	Hmmmm. They're always a problem...and always will be. Right now it's the Lombards that concern me.
BERTRADA:	But they're way down in Italy.
PEPIN:	And they're threatening the pope. The emperor in Constantinople wouldn't help, so he's coming to me, the king of the Franks.
CHARLES:	What are you going to do, Father?
PEPIN:	Send you out to greet him and his entourage.
CHARLES:	Wow! Me? Will we fight for the pope?

PEPIN:	My son, we Franks are Christians, and we must always protect the Church. But we must know what we're fighting for....
FULRAD:	Not the political goals of the pope. Right?
PEPIN:	Right. My son, in political affairs, always make sure the pope knows who's boss.

Scene II: Nobles and Chiefs Assembly, Worms, Frankland, A.D. 772.

OMNRAD:	King Charles, why have you called us together?
CHARLES:	To enlist your support in ending the Saxon menace.
BOKOR:	It's about time! They dishonor our women and destroy our crops.
OMNRAD:	A heavy night of drinking usually gets them going.
BOKOR:	Which for those barbarians is every night.
OMNRAD:	What are your plans?
CHARLES:	Mobilize all our forces, and then strike quickly and deeply into their homeland.
BOKOR:	Will you go after their sacred tree?
CHARLES:	I mean to chop it down myself!
OMNRAD:	Will you have all their leaders killed?
CHARLES:	No. I only wish to teach them a lesson. Besides, they are barbarians, and we must not stoop to their level.
BOKOR:	I don't trust them! They'll promise one thing, then do another. They have no sense of honor.
CHARLES:	Then as Christians we must teach them! That's why I intend to be generous after we subdue them. Now, return to your people and ready them for this campaign.

CHORUS:

I:	This particular threat would soon subside,
II:	And the Saxon leaders promised reform;
III:	But in reality they lied,
IV:	And years of battle were sadly born.
I:	Barbarian ways died hard and tough;
II:	Expedient promises they'd later ignore.
III:	In time, when Charles had had enough,
IV:	Tolerance gave way to merciless war.
I:	When Charles assembled the Saxon chiefs,
II:	Forty-five hundred answered the call;
III:	Forsaking the mercies of Christian beliefs,
IV:	He coldly slaughtered them all.
I:	Each victory enlarged his kingdom,
II:	And in time he grew to be
III:	Christian conqueror of the heathen
IV:	And restorer of Western unity.
I:	Lombards, Bavarians, and Saxons
II:	Were added to the Franks' domain.
III:	But disaster to Charles' squadrons
IV:	Awaited in the Pyrenees of Spain.
I:	He retreated through a mountain gap
II:	From a misguided, hopeless campaign,
III:	And his enemies set a sinister trap
IV:	Upon his rear-guard battle train.
I:	Yet from this ambush tragic
II:	A hero's legend was won:
III:	The age's greatest epic,
IV:	The French jewel, "Song of Roland."

Scene III: Palace school, Frankland, late 780's.

EINHARD: Tell me, teacher Alcuin, who are these two men you brought from Ireland?

ALCUIN: Monks . . . experts in astronomy.

EINHARD: King Charles certainly has a keen interest in that subject.

ALCUIN: Come over and meet them . . . Dungal, Clement, this is Einhard, the king's secretary.

DUNGAL: We're pleased to meet you.

EINHARD: Welcome to you both. I'd like to attend some of your astronomy sessions myself.

CLEMENT: We'd be delighted. Say, aren't you also the king's treasurer?

ALCUIN: And architect?

CLEMENT: Do you really have a welfare system for the poor? One financed by taxes on the rich nobles and clergy?

EINHARD: We certainly do! It's the king's idea. He hates the idea of free men giving up their rights because of poverty. I suppose you two, being monks, don't like a tax on clergy.

DUNGAL: On the contrary . . . it seems most wise and fair.

CLEMENT: Since we're new here, please tell us about King Charles . . . and his interests.

DUNGAL: We're both a bit anxious . . . Charles being a giant and mighty conqueror. . . .

EINHARD: He stands six feet four, and he has been known to knock down a strong horse with one blow of his fist.

ALCUIN: And unbend four horseshoes at a time.

CLEMENT: Maybe we should return to Ireland.

EINHARD: Have no fear. King Charles has an insatiable hunger for all kinds of learning, from math, to music—to logic, to Latin, to law—

ALCUIN: —to theology . . . and, of course, astronomy.

DUNGAL: But does he easily get frustrated, and throw tantrums like some rulers?

EINHARD: He can be gentle as a lamb. He usually takes his lessons with some of his children. And he absolutely adores them.

DUNGAL: What are you getting at?

EINHARD: Simply this: King Charles would never lose his temper around his children. Besides, he never gets drunk. He hates excess of all kinds, in eating, drinking, and dressing.

ALCUIN: Writing does frustrate him, especially the new script he's promoting so much.

EINHARD: The script that's so uniform and beautiful—

ALCUIN: —and clear. King Charles just can't seem to get the handle of it.

EINHARD: He certainly tries! He has tablets under his pillow that he practices on in the middle of the night!

CLEMENT: It sounds as if he's one ruler who truly loves and respects education.

ALCUIN: Indeed, that's why he's brought scholars here from all over Europe.

EINHARD: King Charles hates superstition and ignorance.

ALCUIN: He's trying to get every cathedral and monastery to establish free—yes, free—schools for the sons of free men and serfs alike.

EINHARD: And he's setting up libraries all over his kingdom.

ALCUIN: Which he'll take time to personally inspect, just like his schools.

DUNGAL: What a unique man! I think we'll both enjoy the challenge of being his teacher.

CHORUS:

I:	800 the year, Christmas the day,
II:	The pope accomplished his desire,
III:	Giving Charles a new role to play:
IV:	First emperor of the Holy Roman Empire.

Legacy

CHORUS:

I:	Steward of the Christian flame
II:	In an age mean and dark,
III:	Directing his energies, with the aim
IV:	Of fanning civilization's spark.

I:	Ancient writings he kept alive,
II:	Copied with artful dexterity;
III:	Later he'd help learning to revive,
IV:	Giving birth to the medieval university.

I:	Between the Mediterranean and Atlantic,
II:	As a progressive, linking fortress,
III:	He preserved the connection dynamic,
IV:	And launched the German greatness.

I:	The European unity he created
II:	Would inspire, but not long remain;
III:	Till the twentieth century was fated
IV:	To revive the vision of Charlemagne.

20 Exciting Plays for Medieval History Classes

Feudalism: The Serfs' Fate

Characters

MARCEL, serf   **ALAIN**, village priest
ROGER, Marcel's son   **INGRID**, Viking girl

Scene I: Outside a serf's cottage, France, c. A.D. 985.

MARCEL: My son, come here immediately.

ROGER: Yes, father.

MARCEL: I'm in hot water with the reeve . . . and you are responsible!

ROGER: What do you mean?

MARCEL: The land we're supposed to farm for the lord . . . why haven't you been doing your job?

ROGER: I'm sorry, father.

MARCEL: You are twelve and nearly a man now. So you are expected to do a man's work. If you don't take care of the lord's strips, I must. And that will mean less food on our table!

ROGER: But why should we be forced to work for nothing?

MARCEL: What are you talking about?

ROGER: Over half the work we serfs do is for the lord. We barely have enough time and energy left over to work our puny strips of land.

MARCEL: Where do you get these ideas?

ROGER: We can take our grain only to the lord's miller, who charges a high fee . . . and our flour to his baker, for another fee. . . .

MARCEL: Hold it!

ROGER: We must buy the lord's third-rate beer and wine. We cannot hunt for game. When we fish, our biggest catch must go to the manor kitchen—

MARCEL: Listen to me!

ROGER: If we want to sell something at the market, we must pay still more fees to the lord.

MARCEL: It's my turn now! I'm always paying fees to the lord. You're right . . . I don't like it, but that's the way things are.

ROGER: Why can't we be free to move about, work only our own land, and hunt and fish as we please?

MARCEL: We are not given such possibilities here.

ROGER: Then why don't we leave?

MARCEL: We can't. Besides, where would we go? Outlaws or roving Vikings would rob and kill us all as soon as we were beyond sight of the castle. Don't you understand, we live this way because it's safe and secure.

ROGER: Now I'm the one who doesn't understand.

MARCEL: In all my thirty-five years I have never been more than five miles from the village. Beyond that distance there is no law and order, only murderers and thieves. Our lord protects us from them. In return, we give him our labor and service.

ROGER: Why can't the king keep law and order?

MARCEL: Because he's too weak. Long ago, when Charlemagne was king, there was more law and order. But when he died, things fell apart.

ROGER: I still don't think the system is right.

MARCEL: The system is as God ordered, so accept your fate.

ROGER: Didn't God order all humans to be born the same?

MARCEL: No more questions! I'm just a simple farmer trying to feed his family and keep out of trouble. And that's what you should be doing! Go to the priest with your questions . . . but only after you've finished your work.

Scene II: Outside the village priest's cottage, that evening.

ALAIN: Who goes there?

ROGER: Roger, son of Marcel.

ALAIN: Why are you about after dark? You should be in bed.

ROGER: Please let me in . . . my soul is troubled.

ALAIN: Very well. Let me get a candle . . . come in, my son.

ROGER: Thank you, Friar Alain. My father said I should come to you with my questions.

ALAIN: About God and your salvation?

ROGER: Not exactly.

ALAIN: Hmm. I don't understand. Why else would a twelve-year-old youth seek a priest after dark?

ROGER: Why does my family live in a one-room hovel that leaks when it rains, and is so cold we have to bring in the animals to sleep with us—

ALAIN: —when the lord lives in a castle, eats fine food, and, when he's not off fighting or hunting, lies around all day while you and your family work from sunup to sundown for barely enough to survive on. . . .

ROGER: How do you know my thoughts? You frighten me.

ALAIN: Don't be alarmed. You are not the first child of serfs to question the feudal way of life. Most don't bother to think about it. But once in a while the more clever ones seek me out.

ROGER: And what do you tell them? I cannot accept this system as "God's will."

ALAIN: I'm not one to resort to simple answers, especially for the quick of mind. Consider this: In this life, each and every person owes someone else. Me, I owe to the Church, as we all do. The king owes to his vassals, and they to him. The serfs owe to their lord, and he owes to them.

20 Exciting Plays for Medieval History Classes

ROGER: Order and protection. I've heard all that before.

ALAIN: Of course. Most people owe the same person their entire life's span. The relationship seldom changes. But a few people—like you—with brains and drive, can change masters.

ROGER: How? The laws and customs are very strict.

ALAIN: And tight. But there is a narrow window opening to two choices: You can flee in secret to a town, or flee with honor to the arms of the Church.

ROGER: Tell me more.

ALAIN: If you run away from the manor, and are not caught after a year and a day passes, custom declares you a free man. Most runaways flee to the towns. It is a choice filled with many dangers and hardships.

ROGER: I'll risk them for freedom!

ALAIN: If you're caught, you could lose even more than what you're trying to escape. Some Viking or other barbarian might make you a slave!

ROGER: Not a chance. I will make it beyond the safe walls of a town.

ALAIN: Possibly. But if you did, how would you live? Who would offer you their open door? What trade would accept an outsider like you as an apprentice?

ROGER: What can the Church offer me?

ALAIN: You could become a priest, learn to read and write, and possibly, in time, become a bishop with your own fief.

ROGER: Do you really mean that?

ALAIN: Most certainly. The lord encourages me to find clever young men within his domain to become priests.

ROGER: Why would he do that, since he'll lose workers?

ALAIN: The lord—like all people, high and low, around the manor— is concerned about his salvation. Giving up one of his serf's sons to the Church will bring him a blessing. Do you wish me to speak to the lord on your behalf?

(A voice calls from outside the cottage.)

INGRID: Sanctuary! Sanctuary!

ALAIN: Enter, my child. Who are you?

INGRID: I am Ingrid, daughter of a Viking chieftain.

ROGER: Of all people to seek sanctuary in our village! Vikings have burned, looted, and terrorized our land continuously for many years.

INGRID: I know. I am not proud of what my people have done. That's why I am here.

ALAIN: Will miracles never cease! A Viking with a conscience!

INGRID: You don't think Vikings have feelings?

ALAIN: Of course not; no pagans do.

INGRID: Good priest, you are greatly mistaken.

ROGER: I'm sure even some Vikings question their way of living, and seek changes.

INGRID: The young man is wise beyond his years.

ALAIN: Yes . . . tell me, Ingrid, how did you come to know the Christian church was a place of sanctuary?

INGRID: On one of my father's raids in Ireland he captured a priest.

ROGER: I thought Viking raiders always killed priests.

INGRID: No. This one was a skilled painter, so my father decided to spare him and bring him to our home.

ROGER: And this priest taught you?

INGRID: Yes. First how to paint, and then, in secret, the Christian faith. When I became a believer, the other Viking families became very angry. They gave my father a choice as chief: kill me or abandon me. Because he loved me so, he decided to bring me here to Christian France.

ALAIN: A wise and loving father.

20 Exciting Plays for Medieval History Classes

ROGER: Brave, too. Vikings are as welcome here as the plague.

ALAIN: But you are welcome here in the Church! She offers you peace, security, and opportunity. Roger, hurry home now. We'll discuss your future later. I need to contact the widow Caroline about lodging Ingrid. . . . What a day!

Cordoba, A.D. 976:
Islam's Spanish Jewel

Characters

CHET, Viking
EDRED, English merchant
NILS, Viking chief
HASDAI, Spanish government
   official

SANCHO and **MUSA**, farmers
SUBH, Cordoban housewife
FLORA, Subh's daughter

Scene I: Near a Viking ship, coastal Britain, A.D. 975.

CHET: Halt, English dog! How dare you approach a Viking ship!

EDRED: A present for your wife . . . very colorful . . . hand-painted by Irish monks.

CHET: What do you want?

EDRED: To speak with your chief.

CHET: He's a Viking warrior. Things like this color book do not interest him.

EDRED: I know. I know. But I can offer him something he *will* like. Please get him.

(CHET exits, returns with NILS.)

CHET: This English dog wishes to speak with you.

EDRED: I hear you're sailing for Iberia. Please take me with you.

NILS: What? Do you think I'm running a cruise ship for taking pale Englishmen from their foggy villages to darken in the Spanish sun? You're nuts.

EDRED: No, no. I want to visit Cordoba, that's all.

NILS:	And what can you offer me?
EDRED:	A solemn promise—a promise of securing for you a sword like no other, made of the finest Toledo steel.
NILS:	My present one suits me fine.
EDRED:	This one can shatter yours with one blow, and yet it is sharp enough to split a floating thread.
NILS:	Very interesting . . . and what do you have to trade in order to get this wonderful sword?
EDRED:	Books! The Arabs love books. I've been told the caliph himself has over 400,000 volumes. Cordoba has seventy libraries!
NILS:	This is all nonsense to me, and I doubt I'll ever see my sword. But I like your boldness, so come on aboard.
CHET:	What do *you* want in Spain?
EDRED:	I'm a merchant trader. Some well-educated monks hired me to bring back some special books.
NILS:	Containing what?
EDRED:	We've heard reports that the Arabs have translated ancient Greek philosophers, and created a new mathematics—algebra, I think it's called. My clients also want me to seek out the wonderful medicines the Arabs have created for treating pain and disease.
CHET:	Those things are for others . . . what do *you* want?
EDRED:	My eyes are growing cloudy. I've heard stories about some doctors in Cordoba who can make them better.
NILS:	We sail with the tide. I hope you find a friendly guide once we get there.
CHET:	Welcome wagons aren't waiting for Vikings, anywhere . . . except home. So you'll need plenty of good luck after we've finished our business.

Scene II: Outside Cadiz, Spain, a year later.

EDRED: Good man, would you please direct me to Cordoba.

HASDAI: Certainly. I'm going there myself. Your company would please me. I sense you are a foreigner.

EDRED: A very anxious one, too, being a Christian in Islamic Spain.

HASDAI: You needn't worry here. The government is very tolerant of non-Muslims. I myself am a Jew. My people have prospered under the caliphs.

EDRED: Your business?

HASDAI: An official of Hakam II. I'm on an inspection tour of our postal service. It's an extensive and efficient system, but like all bureaucracies, it requires constant monitoring.

EDRED: So that's why your party is small, and humbly dressed?

HASDAI: Very astute. This way I can learn the truth. And what's your business in Spain?

EDRED: To secure books and medicines for my clients in England.

HASDAI: How will you pay for them?

EDRED: With these books. This one is illustrated by Irish priests. And here's the *Exeter Book*, a collection of English poems.

HASDAI: My friend, you have a treasure here. To an Arab, poetry is more precious than gold. I will help you find customers, and the things you seek.

EDRED: I am most grateful. The journey to Cordoba, is it long and difficult ?

HASDAI: Not at all. It's less than a week by foot.

EDRED: I mean . . . the hazards and uncertainties.

HASDAI: Do not be anxious. Our roads are very safe from brigands and bandits. You will enjoy the journey. We'll follow the Salado River until it joins with the Guadalquivir at Seville. From there to Cordoba it will be like a stroll through a beautiful garden.

20 Exciting Plays for Medieval History Classes

Scene III: Farmland outside Cordoba, a few days later.

EDRED: You told the truth . . . Andalusia is like a lush garden. But how can this be, since we are now quite far from the river?

HASDAI: You've listened to me for days. Let's talk to these farmers, who are old friends of mine. Sancho, Musa, come meet my new English friend.

SANCHO: Hasdai, how good to see you again.

HASDAI: And you two as well. Edred wants to learn about our agriculture.

MUSA: A worthy subject, my friend. Because we farmers produce so much with our efficient system. Cordoba thrives. . . .

SANCHO: . . . opening doors of opportunity to artisans, poets, physicians, and scholars.

MUSA: And long-winded intellectuals!

EDRED: But what accounts for your great crop surplus?

MUSA: Our brains and sweat! And, of course, our great network of irrigation canals.

SANCHO: Don't forget how we enrich the soil with fertilizers.

MUSA: When our Arab and Berber ancestors crossed the strait from Morocco, they brought many ideas and products from the East.

EDRED: Such as?

SANCHO: Rice, buckwheat, and sugarcane—

MUSA: Pomegranates and cotton—

SANCHO: Spinach, asparagus, silk, bananas, cherries, apricots—

EDRED: Amazing!

MUSA: And more—oranges, lemons, quinces, grapefruits—

SANCHO:	Peaches, dates, figs, strawberries, ginger, and even myrrh.
EDRED:	A Garden of Eden! Just one more question about your agriculture. Why haven't I seen any oxen?
MUSA:	Those dawdling beasts? They're too slow and too stubborn.
SANCHO:	We use horses, donkeys, and mules for our plowing and draft work. They're much more efficient.
MUSA:	Speaking of horses...no finer ones exist than ours, from fleet Arabians to sturdy plow breeds.
SANCHO:	Here in Spain, the breeding of horses is an art and a science.
MUSA:	And a consuming passion as well!
EDRED:	Are all the farms in Spain so prosperous?
HASDAI:	Allow me to intervene...I believe you're really asking if we have any poor people.
EDRED:	You're very perceptive.
HASDAI:	In truth, we do. But they are provided for. One quarter of all income from the caliph's own lands is given to them. Let's continue on to Cordoba. Good-bye, Sancho and Musa.

Scene IV: Edge of Cordoba, late that night.

EDRED:	Are all the city's streets so well paved and lit?
HASDAI:	Yes. Notice how the sidewalks are raised.
EDRED:	English streets are dark and muddy.
HASDAI:	Ours are also well policed. In a city of a half million, there is very little crime. This is my sister's home, where we'll spend the night.

Scene V: Home in Cordoba, next morning.

SUBH: Good morning, dear brother and English guest. Would you like to take a full bath before eating?

HASDAI: I don't think so. We'll just freshen up with your water here.

EDRED: Fresh water in your home? How do you do it?

HASDAI: By a large aqueduct that begins far outside the city. Once here, a vast network of pipes carries fresh water to homes, fountains, and public baths throughout the city.

EDRED: How delightfully convenient! But you must pay very high taxes.

SUBH: They are reasonable and fair, just like our laws.

HASDAI: As a government official, may I add that the administration of civic affairs here is both just and efficient.

SUBH: How you brag, dear brother. But he does speak the truth. Citizens take great pride in their city for the simple reason that things get done!

EDRED: Do you have a family?

SUBH: I am a widow with an adult daughter and a younger boy and girl.

EDRED: Are they here now?

SUBH: No. The young ones have already left for school. Flora should soon be returning from the market with lots of fresh fruit.

(Enter FLORA.)

FLORA: Good morning, dear uncle.

HASDAI: Good morning, dear niece. I want you to meet my new friend from England—Edred. He's very interested in books and our culture.

FLORA: Welcome...please have some fresh fruit.

EDRED: Thank you. In England such a basket would cost a king's ransom.

FLORA: Since our markets are well stocked, prices are quite competitive.

HASDAI: And the markets are closely monitored as well. All weights and measures are regularly inspected for accuracy. Flora, will you please accompany Edred to the book market?

FLORA: Certainly. I'll also show you the university. Any other places or people you wish to see?

EDRED: See? Yes...that's a problem I hope to correct here. My eyes are growing cloudy.

FLORA: It sounds as if you might need cataract surgery. Our doctors are very skilled in this area. Christians come from all over Europe seeking treatment here. I'll help arrange an appointment for you tomorrow.

EDRED: Again, many thanks to all of you for your kindness and generosity. I can't believe what a wonderful and civilized place Cordoba is.

HASDAI: Flora, why don't you teach Edred how to play chess while he's here?

FLORA: Of course!

EDRED: Thank you, I would enjoy that. I can see my time here will be pleasant as well as profitable.

William the Conqueror and the Norman Conquest of England

Characters

HAROLD GODWINSON, powerful English Saxon earl
EDWARD (the Confessor), king of England
ROBERT, Norman messenger
WILLIAM, duke of Normandy
ODO (bishop), William's half-brother

LANE, Saxon messenger
GYRTH and **LEOFWINE**, Harold's brothers
TOSTIG, Harold's half-brother
MATILDA, William's wife

Scene I: King's palace, London, England, 1064.

HAROLD: Sire, you wish to see me?

EDWARD: Yes, my good brother-in-law. I'm sending you to my cousin in Normandy.

HAROLD: To William? For what purpose?

EDWARD: To confirm a pledge I made to him some years ago.

HAROLD: What pledge, sire?

EDWARD: God did not see fit to grant me any children. And though William is a Norman, he is my choice as rightful heir to the crown of England.

HAROLD: But aren't you being premature?

EDWARD: Harold, only a few years remain for me on this earth. Godspeed for your journey.

HAROLD: I am your obedient servant.

Scene II: Caen, France,
a few weeks later.

ROBERT: My lord, Count Guy has taken prisoner the Saxon earl, Harold Godwinson.

WILLIAM: Count Guy is a barbarian scoundrel! He'll try to squeeze the Saxon for a fat ransom.

ODO: What would bring the Englishman, Harold, to France?

WILLIAM: To see me, I presume. I want Harold brought safely here immediately.

ODO: I suggest sending some of our more seasoned knights to the greedy count.

WILLIAM: Yes—let them bring him an offer he can't refuse.

Scene III: Bonneville sur
Tourques, days later.

WILLIAM: Harold, you are a most valiant soldier.

HAROLD: It is you, William, who are valiant. You saved me from the clutches of Count Guy.

WILLIAM: But shortly after, you aided me against my Breton enemies. You alone rescued two of my soldiers from certain death.

HAROLD: My honor and duty to serve you.

WILLIAM: Walk with me . . . to a hallowed place.

(They walk on.)

HAROLD: Who are all these men?

(William uncovers a chest of holy relics.)

WILLIAM: Harold, Earl of Wessex, before these barons, and above the bones of saints we stand upon, do you solemnly pledge to support my claim to the throne of England? Swear it! Swear it!

HAROLD: I . . . I . . . yes, my lord.

Scene IV: House of Harold, England, January 5, 1066.

LANE: My lord, King Edward the Confessor is dead.

GYRTH: Brother Harold, the crown awaits you!

LEOFWINE: But what about William, the duke of Normandy?

GYRTH: Our earls will never honor the Norman's claim.

HAROLD: True, indeed. But I must be crowned immediately after Edward is buried.

LEOFWINE: Why the haste?

HAROLD: To unite and prepare our people. Others will rush with violence to claim the throne.

GYRTH: Who besides William?

HAROLD: That Viking viper, Harald Hardraade, king of Norway.

Scene V: Rouen, France, January, 1066.

ROBERT: My lord, King Edward the Confessor is dead.

WILLIAM: My poor cousin. . . . Inform the servants to prepare for the journey to England.

ROBERT: My lord . . . there is more. . . .

WILLIAM: Out with it, man!

ROBERT: Harold Godwinson has already been crowned.

WILLIAM: That treacherous, lying, Saxon dog! He swore before man and God to support my claim.

ROBERT: What will you do? Invade England?

WILLIAM: Of course! For some time I have been mentally preparing for a cross-Channel invasion. Four critical tasks must be met, and number one needs Tostig. Is he close by?

ODO:	He's just outside. I'll bring him in.

(TOSTIG enters.)

TOSTIG:	Yes, my lord.
WILLIAM:	Do you know of your half-brother's treachery?
TOSTIG:	Yes, my lord. I am at your service.
WILLIAM:	Good. Just before I invade England in the south, I want the English armies tied up in the north. Go to Norway and convince their king, Harald Hardraade, of his opportunity. Get him to attack immediately! Be off, then, and Godspeed.

(TOSTIG exits.)

ODO:	Brilliant strategy! The other three tasks?
WILLIAM:	Build an invasion fleet, organize an army, and secure the pope's support.
ODO:	We can do these things. But what do you really think of our chances? Crossing the perilous English Channel, safely landing, securing supplies, and fighting on foreign soil—all these tasks will be difficult.
WILLIAM:	Brother, have you forgotten how thick Viking blood runs in Norman veins? We know how to build sturdy ships, too. But the supply problems greatly worry me.
ODO:	Then we must force Harold Godwinson into a decisive battle immediately after we land.
WILLIAM:	Precisely. Time only increases the Saxon advantage.
ODO:	How will you counteract their sturdy yeoman soldiers?
WILLIAM:	They're very tough fighters. But their battles with the Vikings—coupled with their long journey to meet us— should greatly weaken them. Besides, English wooden shields are no match for Norman cavalry and steel. Call a council of the barons.

(Exit ODO and enter MATILDA.)

MATILDA:	Dear, what is all this invasion talk about?

WILLIAM: The fate of a kingdom.

MATILDA: Oh, don't be so dramatic.

WILLIAM: England's destiny will soon be decided.

MATILDA: Because this man, or that, is king? Come, come, my dear. Kings enter and exit like well-adorned messengers. The people go on living just as before.

WILLIAM: Not this time. Three of us claim the English throne. If Harald Hardraade wins, England will degenerate into a Viking fort for servicing and protecting barbarian marauders. If Harold Godwinson remains on the throne, the Saxons will close off their island like a monastery.

MATILDA: And if William, the duke of Normandy, prevails?

WILLIAM: Then we Normans will bring England all the fruits of European civilization: our learning, language, architecture, system of justice. . . .

MATILDA: May God protect you, my beloved.

Scene VI: King's palace, London, England, September, 1066.

GYRTH: When do you think we'll be attacked?

HAROLD: William is not one to dilly-dally about. Are all the lookouts in place?

LEOFWINE: All coastal posts are manned and ready.

(Enter an anxious messenger.)

LANE: Sire, Harald of Norway has invaded in the north. His Viking forces now occupy York.

HAROLD: Assemble our forces! We must subdue this threat without delay!

20 Exciting Plays for Medieval History Classes

Scene VII: South of York, England, September 25, 1066.

GYRTH: What a stunning and complete victory our forces have won here at Stamford Bridge!

LEOFWINE: Capped by the deserved deaths of the Norwegian king and the traitor Tostig!

HAROLD: Treachery has tasted its bitter fruits. Now, England is forever free of the Viking menace.

(Enter an anxious messenger.)

LANE: Sire, William has invaded in the south! His forces number seven thousand. His knights are burning and pillaging Hastings.

HAROLD: Then we must hurry to stop them! We can't let William's army do further harm to our people!

GYRTH: But brother—our troops are all weary, and many are wounded.

LEOFWINE: And Hastings is over three hundred miles away!

HAROLD: No matter. I'll order forced marches to meet this final challenge to my crown!

Scene VIII: Senlac, near Hastings, October 14, 1066.

LANE: Sire, the enemy assembles on Senlac Hill.

HAROLD: Men of England, now is the time to show your matchless strength and undaunted courage.

GYRTH: The enemy advances. . . .

HAROLD: Close ranks. Keep the shield wall intact. There is no path for retreat!

LEOFWINE: Our men are holding! The Norman cavalry is beaten back. The Normans are now retreating! And our men are madly pursuing them!

HAROLD: No! We must keep the shield wall intact! The retreat is only a Norman trick to scatter our infantry.

LEOFWINE: Our men are scattered all over in the open.

GYRTH: Mounted Norman knights have rushed in from the flanks. They're cutting our infantry to pieces!

LANE: Norman archers are advancing towards us!

GYRTH: We have no more protection!

LEOFWINE: We must stop them from getting any closer!

HAROLD: *(wailing in pain)* I'm struck down! A Norman arrow in my face!

(Norman knights attack and kill HAROLD. WILLIAM and ODO enter, surveying the spoils of battle.)

ODO: William, you have conquered! Harold is dead, and his troops have fallen or scattered. You shall be the king of England!

Genghis Khan (1167?-1227)

Characters

CHORUS I, II, III, IV
YISUGEI, father of Temujin
OELUN EKE, mother of Temujin
TEMUJIN, Genghis Khan

MUKDIN, guide for the Chin envoy
DRECHI and **SOCH**, Mongolian soldiers

Prologue

CHORUS:

I:	Central Asia is a forbidding place;
II:	Winters are long and raw.
III:	A land equal to the hardiest race;
IV:	Survival, its paramount law.
I:	A land to wander, not to settle,
II:	For rare are its ribbons of life-giving grass;
III:	A ceaseless test of everyone's mettle,
IV:	Where only the strong find the courage to pass.
I:	Icy winds and summer dust
II:	Keep her peoples on the go:
III:	Tribes divided by nature's cruel thrust,
IV:	Their unity brief as a summer's snow.
I:	But in the long-ago twelfth century
II:	Did rush upon history's stage
III:	A warrior of cunning and bravery—
IV:	The political genius of his age.

I:	A simple "yurt" tent was his first abode,
II:	Where life was primitive and plain.
III:	From danger and hunger to power he rode:
IV:	An empire larger no other could claim.
I:	Uniting the tribes of Mongolia,
II:	He made China his vassal and pawn;
III:	Turning west, he humbled proud Persia,
IV:	Where he ruled by the name Genghis Khan.

Scene I: Nomad's ordu (tent village), Mongolia, c. 1170.

YISUGEI:	Where is the boy?
OELUN EKE:	Riding the fat woolly sheep.
YISUGEI:	No more time for child's play.
OELUN EKE:	Yes . . . three years is old enough to ride a horse.
YISUGEI:	If he cannot ride, it's no use teaching him to shoot a strong bow. Some day Temujin will take my place as head of the clan. He must be prepared.
OELUN EKE:	He is very strong.
YISUGEI:	A clan leader must never show fear.
OELUN EKE:	Have you prepared the horse?
YISUGEI:	Yes. It's time to test the boy. I'll tie him to the saddle, and then slap the horse.
OELUN EKE:	*(somewhat worried)* And we'll see what happens.

Scene II: A few minutes later.

OELUN EKE:	Did you watch his eyes as he rode?
YISUGEI:	I saw no fear. He even steered the horse.

OELUN EKE:	He's very determined. The ruler of the sky gave him a special nature. Temujin will try to steer everything.

Scene III: Hunting expedition, Mongolia, c. 1176.

YISUGEI:	My son, you have learned well how to ride and hunt.
TEMUJIN:	You have been a good teacher.
YISUGEI:	Now you must learn to survive.
TEMUJIN:	What do you mean? You have watched me. Is there anyone my age who can ride faster or shoot so well a man's bow?
YISUGEI:	No . . . but times will come when there is no game to chase and no fish to catch.
TEMUJIN:	Then I will ride home for food.
YISUGEI:	But you know we often hunt days away from our ordu. Sometimes you must open a vein in your horse's neck and drink.
TEMUJIN:	Won't the horse die?
YISUGEI:	No, but *you* will, without some food.
TEMUJIN:	I understand.
YISUGEI:	But there is more to surviving. You must always be on guard against your enemies.
TEMUJIN:	Who are they?
YISUGEI:	Everyone! Always remember, any Mongolian clan is ready to steal our horses and raid our ordu.
TEMUJIN:	What about our own clan?
YISUGEI:	As leader, you must command absolute loyalty. That is your own true protection.
TEMUJIN:	How do you get it?

YISUGEI:	By always being brave and fair. Show no special favor to anyone. Treat treachery with no mercy. Remember, a leader's first responsibility is to protect his followers. Those you faithfully protect will protect you.
TEMUJIN:	Why can't one leader be the protector of all the Mongol clans, so there wouldn't be any more killing and raiding?
YISUGEI:	My son, you are a dreamer. The clans have always fought each other. Besides, no man is strong enough to be such a leader.
TEMUJIN:	Or wise enough....

Scene IV: Oelun Eke's yurt, days later.

YISUGEI:	Open the yurt! Open the yurt!
OELUN EKE:	What's wrong? Where's Temujin?
YISUGEI:	With the chief of the Khonigirad clan. He's found a wife... send for him at once!
OELUN EKE:	Your belly moves like a raging river!
YISUGEI:	I've been poisoned!
OELUN EKE:	Who poisoned you?
YISUGEI:	Some Tartars who gave me overnight shelter. What treachery! It's not safe for Temujin. My enemies will now go after him.
OELUN EKE:	You must rest....
	(YISUGEI falls asleep briefly, then wakes.)
YISUGEI:	Is Temujin here? I must talk to him and—
OELUN EKE:	I've sent a messenger on the fastest horse.
YISUGEI:	My stomach's on fire! Tell Temujin....

Scene V: Hours later.

TEMUJIN:	Father!
OELUN EKE:	He is dead. We must leave this place at once.
TEMUJIN:	Why? Surely the many clans father ruled over will protect us.
OELUN EKE:	I've talked with the chiefs. They are deserting us.
TEMUJIN:	Why? Father protected them. He said they were all loyal.
OELUN EKE:	To him, yes—a strong leader and fierce warrior. But they won't give their allegiance to his nine-year-old son, or to me, his wife.
TEMUJIN:	What are we going to do?
OELUN EKE:	Flee—before our enemies find out we're abandoned.
TEMUJIN:	On my father's spirit I swear our clan will one day be so strong, so mighty, that my name will strike fear and respect wherever it's sounded!

Scene VI: Mongol army headquarters, on the border of the Chin Empire, late 1210.

MUKDIN:	Hey, soldiers. Can I talk with you?
DRECHI:	Are you with the Chin envoy?
MUKDIN:	Only as a guide, forced into service. I'm just curious. . . .
SOCH:	About what?
MUKDIN:	Genghis Khan. How long have you been with him?
DRECHI:	Me? I go way back . . . to the time he began rebuilding his own clan.
SOCH:	I was in the next clan to accept his leadership.
MUKDIN:	You mean Genghis Khan built this great army from nothing but himself?

20 Exciting Plays for Medieval History Classes

DRECHI:	That's about right . . . clan by clan.
MUKDIN:	Excuse a simple man's interest . . . but how? How could he even start to unite all Mongolia?
SOCH:	As a young warrior he had no equal.
DRECHI:	He could outride, outshoot, and outsuffer any man.
SOCH:	And outthink!
DRECHI:	Yes! Right after his father's murder an enemy clan captured him. He was only nine or ten.
SOCH:	They put a board behind his neck and hung his arms through holes.
DRECHI:	He was supposed to suffer one night like that before they killed him the next morning.
MUKDIN:	What happened?
SOCH:	He used the board to knock out his captor, and then fled.
MUKDIN:	They must have hunted him.
DRECHI:	They certainly did! He hid in some bushes, then in water when his enemies drew close.
SOCH:	When darkness came he resumed his escape, finally stumbling into my father's ordu. My father quickly befriended this stranger. They have been very close ever since.
DRECHI:	It was daring feats like his amazing escape that inspired his own clan to follow him, even when he was young.
MUKDIN:	But the other clans . . . how did Genghis Khan get them to accept his leadership?
DRECHI:	He rebuilt his own clan into a mean, fast, and very organized fighting force.
SOCH:	As his reputation spread, he'd make other clans a simple proposition: follow me and I will protect you and give you a fair share of all conquests.
MUKDIN:	And what did he promise if they didn't?

20 Exciting Plays for Medieval History Classes

DRECHI: They would be completely destroyed or enslaved. Those who hear him immediately sense that his threats are not idle, and his promises are not empty.

SOCH: Genghis Khan gushes confidence and power like a mighty fountain.

MUKDIN: And thirsty chiefs eagerly drink. I understand the source of his personal power, but what makes his armies so formidable?

DRECHI: His troops are absolutely loyal.

SOCH: They're also tough, highly skilled, and very disciplined.

MUKDIN: But battles are usually very chaotic. Things quickly get out of control.

DRECHI: Not with his armies! Like the great hunts he leads in the Gobi, his strategy is always the same: encircle the enemy.

SOCH: And he uses convincing tactics of deception. He tricks the enemy into a trap.

DRECHI: No army has better communications. We use ingenious signals to coordinate all troop movements.

SOCH: And our sappers are the finest in the world!

MUKDIN: Your what?

SOCH: Sappers ... our engineers. They're experts in setting traps, sabotage, and construction, especially siege weapons.

DRECHI: Some are from conquered peoples.

SOCH: Our leader is very, very tough, but his head is not full of rocks!

DRECHI: He has learned and borrowed many tactics from our enemies.

MUKDIN: I'm very impressed. But the Chin have more troops, and their cities are protected by huge walls and strong forts.

SOCH: No matter. We are united, and the enemy is not.

DRECHI: And our sappers are already busy at work!

MUKDIN: Rumors say the envoy I guided will ask Genghis Khan to publicly kowtow to the new Chin emperor.

SOCH: Never! He will spit towards his palace instead. In time Genghis Khan will have all China kowtowing to *him*!

CHORUS:

I: In time China fell to the Mongol hordes,

II: In a manner both fierce and sure.

III: Then Genghis sought trade with Persian lords;

IV: No conflict he wished to stir.

I: But his envoys were treated with utmost contempt,

II: Then cruelly murdered on the spot;

III: The Khan, with his patience fully spent,

IV: Gathered his armies to avenge this blot.

I: Westward they hurled their lightning wars,

II: Felling all enemies in the way;

III: From the Caspian to the Pacific shores,

IV: Genghis Khan held absolute sway.

Epilogue and Legacy

CHORUS:

I: The empire for many years held fast,

II: A trade bridge between East and West,

III: Where ideas and commerce conveniently passed,

IV: Rousing Europe from its medieval rest.

I: Russia was shaped by Mongol swords

II: In a dark, autocratic mold;

III: All Europe lay gripped by Asian hordes

IV: Who then strangely released their hold.

I: Returning to their ancient homeland,
II: Their legacy proved to be
III: Not a building, or a culture grand,
IV: But the most vast destruction in history.

I: Western Asia was the hardest struck,
II: Reduced to grim necessity,
III: Leaving a culture sadly stuck
IV: In centuries of impotence and poverty.

20 Exciting Plays for Medieval History Classes

Clare's Story:
Francis of Assisi

Characters

MARIA, nun
CLARE, founder of "Poor Clares"
DONNA and **GINA**, nuns
FRANCIS
GUIDO and **THOMAS**, friends of
Francis

BISHOP
PIERO, father of Francis
FREDO and **PAULO**,
Gubbio villagers

Scene I: San Damiano,
Italy, 1246.

MARIA: Sister Clare, we have brought you a special gift.

CLARE: Thank you, but you know I cannot accept it. Have you forgotten our poverty oath?

DONNA: Of course not. Please accept it.

CLARE: No. But show it to me so I'll know which needy person can best use it.

GINA: Here you are. . . .

(MARIA, DONNA, and GINA cup their ears.)

CLARE: *(laughing)* You look like three donkeys holding your ears like that.

MARIA: It's our gift . . . please fill our ears with stories about Francis.

DONNA: Yes. You knew him. Tell us what he was like.

CLARE: He certainly would have smiled at your "gift." Let's see, now . . . Francis was always so full of joy and humor. . . . Oh, and how he loved animals!

GINA:	What was he like before he became Brother Francis?
MARIA:	Did he really dress like a peacock?
DONNA:	Was he always full of pranks and mischief?
GINA:	Did he spend his rich father's money like the "prodigal son"?
CLARE:	Oh, you young new sisters! I thought your gift was ears, not voices.
MARIA:	We're sorry, Sister Clare. We'll listen.
CLARE:	Brother Francis was the greatest person I ever knew. All the good work we do, here and beyond, started with him. He was completely devoted to God, and to helping people . . . anyone in need.
DONNA:	But he wasn't like that when he was young.
CLARE:	You are partly right. To understand Francis, you must know his parents. His mother was French. She gave him a tender heart, and taught Francis knightly manners.
GINA:	And his father?
CLARE:	A rich, self-made merchant, consumed by ambition for a higher social position.
MARIA:	He pushed his son up the ladder of status?
CLARE:	Precisely. As long as Francis mingled with the right crowd, the sons and daughters of the nobility, no behavior was out of bounds.
DONNA:	None? He was that spoiled? That indulged?
CLARE:	Yes. Let me just tell you of one incident. . . .

Scene II: (Flashback) Assisi, Italy, c. 1198.

FRANCIS:	Guido, Thomas—my main cavaliers! What's on the table of earthly delights for tonight?
GUIDO:	Nothing, man . . . pure famine.

20 Exciting Plays for Medieval History Classes

THOMAS:	Only dry bones, even the crumbs are gone.
GUIDO:	Everyone's asleep in this boring dump.
FRANCIS:	Then let's give its dull citizenry an entertaining reason for rousing!
THOMAS:	I don't feel like any of your fighting knights' games.
GUIDO:	Me neither. That's old stuff, anyway.
FRANCIS:	Well, *this* isn't. Here's my plan. First, we go out to Farmer Nicolo's fields and set fire to his haystacks.
THOMAS:	I like it! I hate that old hoghead.
FRANCIS:	Then we come back to the tanner's shop and madly beat his cauldrons like drums.
GUIDO:	Not many will sleep through that!
FRANCIS:	When everyone's up and about, we'll pour my dad's best wine into the gutter, and watch the town bums dive for it. What do you think?
GUIDO:	The famine of boredom is no more! Let's go for it!

Scene III: San Damiano, 1246.

GINA:	How could Francis be so cruel! First to his father, and then to those poor men lapping up the wine?
CLARE:	It's hard to understand, I know. But Francis was always a very complicated person. Until he found inner peace and direction, he remained a whirlwind of passions and aimless energies.
MARIA:	What happened after this escapade?
CLARE:	His father paid off the farmer, and bailed Francis out of jail.
DONNA:	Was Francis always so indulged?
CLARE:	Yes. As long as Francis aspired to be a great knight, and mixed with the nobility, all was forgiven—all debts and fines paid.
GINA:	So...how and when did Francis' long party come to an end?

CLARE:	Soon after this incident Francis went off to war. He was captured, imprisoned, and forced to live in the most wretched conditions. After his release his moods and behavior became even more bizarre and unusual than before.
MARIA:	For instance?
CLARE:	One day he invited the lowliest people, the dregs of Assisi, to a lavish banquet.
DONNA:	And what happened?
CLARE:	They came, all right...laughed in his face, and then proceeded to trash his house.
GINA:	Had Francis now left all his old friends?
CLARE:	Just about. He began spending most of his time with poor farm workers.
MARIA:	Did he really kiss a leper?
CLARE:	Yes...but that comes later.
DONNA:	You still haven't told us when and why Francis' father stopped indulging him.
CLARE:	It was after a vision Francis had. He'd been spending a lot of time in the old, run-down chapel nearby, and on one visit he had a vision. The vision instructed him to restore this and other decrepit churches.
GINA:	Why was the chapel in such poor condition?
CLARE:	You must remember that before Francis came along most of the priests neglected the poor and common people.
MARIA:	You mean, the Church didn't care?
CLARE:	To Francis it seemed that the Church had forgotten what the Gospel was about. After all, Jesus had lived and taught amongst the poor. Francis believed that his mission was to remind the Church of these truths.
DONNA:	So...how did he?
CLARE:	He started repairing the church. But when he took his father's money for the project, matters came to a head.

Scene IV: (Flashback) Bishop's court, Assisi, c. 1206.

BISHOP: Master Bernardone, why have you hauled your son into this court?

PIERO: To publicly humiliate him! And to get my hard-earned money back!

BISHOP: What money?

PIERO: The money he steals from me and gives to no-good beggars and parasites...and to silly old priests for repairing the roofs on abandoned country chapels. I'll be broke in no time if he doesn't stop!

BISHOP: Francis, what do you have to say for yourself?

FRANCIS: Here, father, is your money. And since you bought me these clothes, you can have them as well. Now, the scales are balanced.

BISHOP: Bernardone! Your son is standing naked in a church court and you do nothing! Francis, quick, put on this old gardener's cloak!

FRANCIS: Gladly...and thank you, good bishop. I shall need no other covering. Farewell.

Scene V: San Damiano.

GINA: Francis was certainly brave...and bold!

MARIA: I suppose many thought him a crazy fool.

CLARE: You're both right.

DONNA: What did Francis do after leaving the court?

CLARE: First, he begged for stones to rebuild churches.

GINA: Aren't most people annoyed by beggars?

CLARE: They are. But people easily sensed a difference about Francis ...that he was really begging for their benefit, and not his own.

MARIA:	And that's why he attracted so many people?
CLARE:	Precisely. Francis made people feel good about themselves. He never put them down; instead, he raised their spirits by sharing his joy and hope.
DONNA:	Weren't most of the people he mixed with very poor?
CLARE:	Yes. And he lived as humbly as they did. But he showed the poor something they had forgotten, or overlooked, about life.
DONNA:	What's that?
CLARE:	The priceless joy and happiness life offers to all, rich and poor . . . in flowers, stars, sunshine, animals, even rocks . . . and menial work. . . .
GINA:	But life can often be so hard and unfair. People can be so cruel and violent.
CLARE:	Francis was very well acquainted with the dark side of life. That's why he could so easily identify with people. He knew suffering and meanness. But he also knew much about grace, understanding, and the power of love.
DONNA:	Do you have another story about Francis?
CLARE:	Yes, and it's my favorite. Remember, Francis loved all of creation. He even liked talking with animals. Well, one day when he was walking to the village of Gubbio. . . .

Scene VI: (Flashback) Gubbio, Italy, c. 1215.

FRANCIS:	Why are you two the only men about?
FREDO:	We're all afraid.
PAULO:	A vicious wolf is terrorizing our village.
FREDO:	Our strongest men have yet to subdue him.
PAULO:	We've tried clubs, stones, and knives. They are no match for this horrible beast.
FRANCIS:	Where does this wolf live?

20 Exciting Plays for Medieval History Classes

FREDO: When he's not stalking our village, he lives in the woods over there.

FRANCIS: I must go to him.

PAULO: No, no, Brother Francis! I know you talk to birds, and little lambs follow at your command, but. . . .

Scene VII: In the forest, moments later.

FRANCIS: Brother Wolf, come here. Good. Brother Wolf, I've heard terrible stories about you. I know you only do these things because you're hungry and fear men. Brother Wolf, will you promise not to harm any of the people of Gubbio if they feed you? Give me your paw to show you agree. Good!

Scene VIII: In the village, moments later.

FREDO: Here comes the wolf! Quickly hide!

(FRANCIS leads the wolf into the village.)

FRANCIS: Have no fear. Have no fear. Brother Wolf has solemnly promised no more harm to Gubbio if you will only feed him and treat him kindly.

FREDO: Brother Francis, are you really sure about this?

FRANCIS: Without hesitation. Have faith, my friends.

PAULO: We will. And we promise to feed this wolf for the rest of his earthly days.

Scene IX: San Damiano.

MARIA: Did the wolf of Gubbio keep his promise?

CLARE: He certainly did! And so did the villagers! Each family kept a little food out for him.

DONNA: And the wolf never bothered anyone?

CLARE:	Not at all. In fact, he became almost like a pet.
GINA:	How long did the wolf live?
CLARE:	Over two more years, until old age caused his peaceful death.
MARIA:	Tell us more, please!
CLARE:	You just don't want to get on with your work! When you're all finished, I'll tell you some more about Francis.
DONNA:	Thank you, Sister Clare.
GINA:	We'll work especially fast!

Mansa Musa and the Glories of the Mali Empire

Characters

PAULO, Venetian trader
AMAL, West African metals broker
KALI, Mali government official
MUSA, king of Mali
BEKK, Mali government official

RANAL, Egyptian official
MALIK, Egyptian sultan
SAHELI, Moorish architect
AMIR, Egyptian scholar

Scene I: Timbuktu, West Africa, 1324.

PAULO: Good friend, are you going to the capital?

AMAL: Yes. Would you like to accompany me?

PAULO: Very much so, since this is my first visit to the kingdom of Mali. I covet your knowledge of its geography and customs.

AMAL: And I welcome your companionship for the journey. What is your business in the capital?

PAULO: To purchase metals for my Venetian clients.

AMAL: You've certainly come to the right place. Niani has large gold, silver, and copper markets. I, myself, am a broker.

PAULO: What good fortune! But I must confess I'm very anxious about security conditions . . . an occupational hazard. Can I enlist honest and competent guards here?

AMAL: Do not be anxious. Your own two guards are sufficient. I only suggest that you secure an experienced guide for the return trip.

PAULO: Are you kidding? I'll be making some very large purchases.

AMAL: My friend, Mali's prosperity rests on two pillars. Trade is the first. The government does everything possible to promote and protect commercial confidence. And that, of course, means open, safe, and honest markets.

PAULO: It sounds as if the kingdom has wise administrators.

AMAL: And very efficient ones, too. The present ruler, Mansa Musa, is committed to improving and enriching the lives of his subjects.

PAULO: You stated that the empire rests on two pillars. What's the other one?

AMAL: Agriculture. Mansa Musa's grandfather, King Sundiata the Great, is responsible for its great expansion.

PAULO: How? Through conquest?

AMAL: Not exactly. He made sure his soldiers were well trained in more than just warfare. He made them farmers, skilled at planting many different crops, and raising cattle and poultry.

PAULO: The people I've seen certainly look healthy.

AMAL: And why not? Even the poorest eat an adequate and balanced diet.

PAULO: Who would have thought such an orderly and prosperous kingdom existed in West Africa?

AMAL: A kingdom equal in land size to all of western Europe.

Scene II: Royal palace, Niani, Mali, 1324.

KALI: Great Mansa, all preparations for the pilgrimage are complete.

MUSA: And our itinerary? Refresh my memory.

BEKK: Northeast across the Sahara to Egypt, then southeast to the holy cities of Medina and Mecca.

MUSA: About two thousand miles, correct?

KALI: Correct.

MUSA: Are you certain that the supplies are adequate for a traveling party of sixty thousand?

KALI: Yes, for the journey and return.

MUSA: Very good...and the gold?

BEKK: Five hundred men will precede you, each carrying a six-pound solid gold staff.

KALI: And behind you will be eighty camels, each bearing three hundred pounds of gold dust.

MUSA: My mount and commissary?

BEKK: Your favorite Arabian stallion, and your favorite cooks.

MUSA: Excellent. But let us never forget the purpose of our journey. We make the *hajj* as devout Muslims, and our generosity along the way should only reflect our devotion. We are not making this pilgrimage for political considerations.

Scene III: Royal palace, Egypt, 1324.

RANAL: The emperor of Mali has arrived! Never have I seen so great a caravan. It's endless!

MALIK: What are you babbling about? I thought he was just another chief from a petty black African tribe.

RANAL: Some tribe, great Sultan! There are thousands of them! Warriors, scholars, cooks, artisans. And gold! Never has Egypt seen so much! Even the pharaohs would have been impressed.

MALIK: Maybe so...but this visiting Mansa had better remember where his feet now stand. This is my domain! And he would be most wise to pay me the proper homage.

RANAL: His emissaries have already expressed their ruler's gratitude to you.

MALIK: Now we're getting somewhere.

RANAL: And they have also expressed Mansa Musa's adamant refusal to bow before any man, slave or sultan.

20 Exciting Plays for Medieval History Classes

MALIK: What! Who does he think he is! If he doesn't bow before me, all my authority and prestige will be challenged. He *must* bow!

RANAL: He's a very proud and determined man.

MALIK: And I . . .? He will bow! Call out the army!

RANAL: Wait . . . we have learned that Mansa Musa is a most generous, peaceful, and sophisticated leader. But he is also a great warrior with a very formidable army behind him. It would be most unwise to threaten him.

MALIK: A "lose-lose" situation, is that what you mean?

RANAL: No . . . I see a way to cut this Gordian knot. Let's arrange a meeting time just before the muezzin begins his call to prayer.

MALIK: Brilliant! As Mansa Musa bows to Mecca to pray, we can claim he paid me the proper homage.

Scene IV: Mecca, Arabia, weeks later.

KALI: Great Mansa, I present you Es-Saheli, the great Moorish architect and scholar.

MUSA: Thank you for meeting me. I have heard you are indeed a master builder, without peer.

SAHELI: You are most kind . . . and your reputation as a noble leader and great patron of learning extends far beyond your realm. What is your desire?

MUSA: To erect great buildings for my people.

SAHELI: And not for your own glory?

MUSA: I appreciate your candor. I have often dealt with fools and schemers who offer me their sweet poison of self-serving flattery.

SAHELI: And what do you do about them?

MUSA: Throw it right back so they choke and retch on their own deceit! It is true—I would like a great palace. But I also seek a great university and mosque for my people. Come with me to Mali and build these great buildings.

SAHELI: Your honesty and humor have moved me. Yes, I will go.

Scene V: Cairo, Egypt, 1325.

BEKK: Great Mansa, I present you Ibn Amir Hajib, the great Egyptian scholar.

AMIR: This is a great personal honor for me.

MUSA: And for me as well...but I don't think all of Egypt is pleased with our return visit.

AMIR: Your generous gifts of gold have unsettled our precious metals markets. Prices have plummeted.

MUSA: Most unfortunate. My advisors inform me that you have some questions about our government.

AMIR: Yes, I do...but what most concerns me is how political power is transferred.

MUSA: It's rather complicated, but heritage is a prime factor.

AMIR: How did you become the Mansa?

MUSA: My predecessor simply relinquished power to me.

AMIR: Why? Was he growing old and feeble?

MUSA: On the contrary, he was full of good health. He was about to sail west across the great sea to new lands. Knowing the voyage's great uncertainty, he thought it most prudent to pass his power on before he embarked.

AMIR: In other words, he went crazy.

MUSA: You do not think there are new lands west of Africa?

AMIR: I doubt that there are, but I am not closed-minded.

MUSA: Maybe you wrongly assume that black African sailors are incapable of long voyages? Do not underestimate our nautical skills.

AMIR: Well, what happened? Did he ever return?

MUSA: Never. But I'm confident that some of his ships reached the new lands and remained there. Someday we'll know the full story.

AMIR: Someday. . . .

20 Exciting Plays for Medieval History Classes

The Black Death, 1347-1349

Scene I: Harbor area, Kaffa, the Crimea (Russia), early 1347.

TOMA: I've never seen anything like it!

LUCA: We had better get on board before we all catch it!

ALDO: Why are you two running? I thought sailors in port always returned to their ship staggering . . . like donkeys walking backwards. Ha!

TOMA: Captain, we're both very sober. A terrible sickness has overtaken Kaffa.

LUCA: All over the city people are dying.

ALDO: Describe it to me.

TOMA: First come painful swellings—

LUCA: In the neck, under the arms, and in the groin.

TOMA: And then, in five days, *death.*

ALDO: Round up all of our men! We must leave port within an hour, not a second later!

LUCA:	We can't possibly find all the crew in so little time! How can we manage without them?
ALDO:	It's too bad! We're leaving regardless. We'll do what we must!
TOMA:	Captain, you know something, don't you?
ALDO:	Yes...I'm sure it's plague. We haven't seen it in Italy for four hundred years. But the old women still recite stories about it ...it can kill by the thousands! Now, go get us a crew!

Scene II: An hour later.

KRUS:	Captain, haven't you forgotten something? You're setting sail, but you haven't loaded on my furs.
ALDO:	Keep your rotten Russian furs! We're returning to Genoa at once!
KRUS:	But you are under a contract!
ALDO:	Keep that, too! Get another buyer.
KRUS:	I don't understand. Why all the haste? My delivery men will be here in two hours.
ALDO:	Fine, you wait here for death, because I'm not! Take my advice and forget your furs. Otherwise the only good they'll do you is to wrap your corpse like fish in the market!
KRUS:	What are you talking about? We had a deal!
ALDO:	There's plague in Kaffa, you boulder-brain! And for this Genoese sailor, that means all deals are off...and so am I.

Scene III: Marseilles, France, late 1347.

MARCEL:	Louis, how's business? Made any big deals lately?
LOUIS:	Doctor, how can you ask such things in times like these?
MARCEL:	Simple. If I don't, I'll go crazy. Everywhere I turn, I see only chaos and misery. Already over a third of the population has died.

20 Exciting Plays for Medieval History Classes

LOUIS: Do you have any idea what is causing this?

MARCEL: Not really. No doctor in Marseilles has seen its like before. Not even our medical manuals have given us a clue.

LOUIS: There is no hope, no remedies?

MARCEL: Remedies? I've seen my share.

LOUIS: Thank goodness! I'll pay anything you ask. Just tell me and my family what to do.

MARCEL: I've seen some people try indulging in wild living, or dancing without stopping.

LOUIS: Does it work? Have those people been spared?

MARCEL: Others have tried special diets or certain sleeping positions.

LOUIS: Describe them in detail! I must know!

MARCEL: Some burn aromatic woods and herbs, or take potions made from gold and pearls.

LOUIS: I'll bring you gold and pearls, and plenty more for you as a reward. Just mix the right potion!

MARCEL: Louis, Louis, my friend. None of these remedies will work. They're only the delusions of the desperate. The only thing that's certain is five horrible days, and then death.

LOUIS: Is there anything—anything—we can do?

MARCEL: Yes. Flee with your family to the countryside. The death rate seems lower there than in the crowded cities. Other than that, we might as well ask this gypsy here. Her advice would be no more useful than any doctor's.

(Enter SYENA.)

LOUIS: Old woman, do you have something to protect me from the great sickness?

SYENA: What does the "learned doctor" prescribe?

LOUIS: He has been very honest with me, and says nothing really works.

SYENA:	Are you so desperate that you would trust a gypsy? Your people despise me and accuse my people of being swindlers and liars. Why do you ask my advice now?
LOUIS:	Because this great sickness respects no one. It's the great equalizer of all our social and racial differences.
SYENA:	Look out on the busy harbor. What do you see?
LOUIS:	Ships from many different places.
SYENA:	Doctor, where did the great sickness first strike?
MARCEL:	Let me think. Why, in ports like Marseilles.
SYENA:	Where in the port cities?
MARCEL:	In the harbor areas.
SYENA:	Yes. Death rides in those crowded ships.
MARCEL:	Of course the sailors get sick, too. You've told us nothing, old woman. Let's leave, Louis.
SYENA:	*(calling after the men as they leave)* It's not the men in the ships that bring death. It's the rats. The rats. . . .

Scene IV: Peasant village, southern England, 1348.

MAGGIE:	Can you believe the prices today?
BABS:	At least *something* good has come from the plague.
MAGGIE:	We bought a good milker and a healthy sow for less than half the usual price.
BABS:	And did you know my man Jack just asked the lord to double his wages?
MAGGIE:	Did he get his ears boxed for it, too?
BABS:	No, Maggie! With so few laborers left, all the big farmers and lords are caught in a pickle!
MAGGIE:	I get it. Pay up, or watch the crops rot. Right?

20 Exciting Plays for Medieval History Classes

BABS:	Yes . . . and about time, too. We common folk have suffered long enough. You know what else Jack said about the farms?
MAGGIE:	No. What's that?
BABS:	They're only going to farm the best land, and let the rest of it go.
MAGGIE:	That should make Jack's work easier.
BABS:	That's right. Say, how are you keeping the plague away?
MAGGIE:	By not letting any strangers cross my doorway.
BABS:	Sounds sensible. Me, I'm a-scrubbing and a-cleaning all day, like my sister who works up at the castle.
MAGGIE:	Waste of time and energy.
BABS:	Maybe so, but it keeps my mind off that horrible sickness.

Scene V: Writers' supply shop, Florence, Italy, 1348.

GIAN:	Hey, Bocca, what do you need all that paper for?
BOCCA:	I'm going to write many stories.
GIAN:	What? In times like these? Half of Florence has already died of the plague.
BOCCA:	Including my dear mother.
GIAN:	Are you going to write about her? We've had enough sadness, don't you think?
BOCCA:	Yes. These stories are going to make people laugh again. I'm going to poke my pen at some people who deserve to be made fun of.
GIAN:	Like wayward clerics and pompous cuckolds?
BOCCA:	Most certainly! I think I'll even write some stories that will make people blush.

GIAN:	That would be a welcome sight! We've stared at the pale faces of death for too long. Tell me, how do you plan to organize these stories?
BOCCA:	I'll have ten people, all fleeing the plague, on an outing in the countryside. To pass the time, once a day each person must tell a story, but no sad ones are allowed. The outing will last for ten days.
GIAN:	Do you have a title yet?
BOCCA:	Yes. "The Decameron," or "Ten Days' Entertainments."
GIAN:	You'll have to write one hundred stories! Good luck, and thank you for the business. I've had precious little lately.
BOCCA:	And thank you. I'll be sure to bring you a copy of my book.
GIAN:	Wonderful! I'll certainly enjoy reading something new like this in Italian.

Scene VI: Village in Rhineland, Germany, August, 1349.

THIKKE:	What is it, girl? Why are you out of breath?
HILDE:	I've just come from the market . . . they're here!
THIKKE:	Daughter, who are you talking about? You act as if it's the Second Coming, and with all the disciples to boot!
HILDE:	The Flagellant Brethren!
THIKKE:	What?
HILDE:	A hundred men singing and marching.
THIKKE:	What do they look like?
HILDE:	They have hoods over their heads, and long white robes with a red cross on the front and back . . . and they carry these awful-looking whips.
THIKKE:	Let's go see who these fellows are.

Scene VII: Town square, a short while later.

RUUDE: In the Lord's precious name, we greet you. THE GREAT PLAGUE IS COMING!

KRULE: As God's punishment for our sins!

RUUDE: To show our sorrow and shame, words of repentance are not enough. We must demonstrate our sincerity.

HILDE: Father! They're tearing their own flesh! They'll all bleed to death!

THIKKE: Their whips are studded with iron spikes! What courage! Daughter, we must listen to these men.

RUUDE: Our suffering is not sufficient. The bearers of the plague must be punished!

THIKKE: Who? Who are they?

KRULE: They poison your wells! They suck your blood in usury!

RUUDE: They killed our Lord!

KRULE: Round up all your Jews!

RUUDE: Hanging is too good for them! Impale them!

THIKKE: Yes! Yes! I'll get my pitchfork!

HILDE: Father! No! These men are cruel and evil liars! Father! Don't go with the mob! Good heavens, is this plague the end of the world?

Epilogue

CHORUS:

I: No, the Black Death did not end the world,

II: Though Europe lost one in four,

I: And those who survived it fitfully hurled

II: Themselves upon feudalism's crumbling door.

I:	And so accelerated a system's demise:
II:	The chains of serfdom creaked and cracked,
I:	Loosening the peasantry to follow their eyes
II:	To towns where thousands would never look back.
I:	From the ashes of the Black Death
II:	A commanding culture would blaze;
I:	Fanned by freedom's undying breath,
II:	Western Europe greeted its dynamic phase.

Joan of Arc
(1412–1431)

Characters

CHORUS I, II, III, IV
YVETTE and **MARIE**, French
  peasants
GOVERNOR (Baudricourt)
JOAN
BERTRAND, French knight

CHARLES, the dauphin
TREMOILLE, advisor to
  Charles
REGNAULT, church official
ALENÇON, French knight
LA HIRE, French soldier

Prologue

CHORUS:

I:	France, France, oh beloved France,
II:	Cruel victim of misery and shame,
III:	Cowering under the English lance,
IV:	Crying over your own dark blame.
I:	The crown, whose crown? Its owners in truth,
II:	England's claim weighs heavy with might,
III:	And Burgundy adds to that corrupted proof,
IV:	Casting France into a hundred years' night.
I:	War! War! Thirteen thirty-seven the start,
II:	Your land the bitter battleground;
III:	"Glory" and greed tear you apart
IV:	For a century and more, till peace be found.
I:	How many towns looted and torched?
II:	How many soldiers wounded and killed?

III:	How many farms pillaged and scorched?
IV:	How many graves did the innocent fill?
I:	Where welled Honor, and gushed forth Right?
II:	Who had the courage to cleanse France's scars?
III:	Who had the will to drown lethargy's might?
IV:	Who had a spirit that reached to the stars?
I:	A phalanx of brave knights of noble renown?
II:	One churchman, well-spoken and unafraid?
III:	Rich men, steadfast under virtue's crown?
IV:	No—a simple, pious, and humble maid.

Scene I: Domremy, France, c. 1424.

YVETTE:	They did it again! I could kill them all!
MARIE:	Burgundian soldiers?
YVETTE:	No, just the usual riffraff from across the river.
MARIE:	What did they do this time? Burn your barn?
YVETTE:	No, but they did steal two of our best cattle. My boys scared them off before they could do worse.
MARIE:	When will it ever end? Aren't we all French? To think that in the next village live our worst enemies. It's absolutely disgusting!
YVETTE:	Politics . . . dirty, rotten politics . . . that's all it is.
MARIE:	All because Burgundy supports the English.
YVETTE:	They were bought off, you mean. And because our village supports the French king, our neighbors think they can do anything to us.
MARIE:	Two enemies . . . the English and Burgundians.
YVETTE:	If only we could unite, the English would be driven out, and we'd have law and order.

20 Exciting Plays for Medieval History Classes

MARIE:	I'd almost be content just to see the French treat each other with some compassion.
YVETTE:	Fat chance. The long war has corrupted and hardened us all...and for a long, long time.
MARIE:	I still think there's some hope for the future. Just look at Jacques and Isabelle's daughter.
YVETTE:	Joan? The tomboy?
MARIE:	Do you know she willingly sleeps on the hard floor so refugees can use her bed?
YVETTE:	If only the next generation would be so unselfish. France might then again be France.
MARIE:	You know the old prophecy...France will be ruined by a woman, and saved by a maiden.
YVETTE:	I hope you're not expecting that of Joan! She can't even read or write. And besides, what important person would ever listen to a peasant girl?
CHORUS:	

I:	Voices, Joan heard voices,
II:	Telling of her destined role.
III:	Not a feast of teenage choices,
IV:	But a brave, impossible goal:

I:	To usher forth the dauphin's coronation
II:	In Reims, so cowardly delayed,
III:	And rally forth a besieged French nation,
IV:	In virtue fierce, in battle unafraid.

I:	But who would listen to a maiden's plea
II:	For help in a mission so bold?
III:	In her heart, she held Honor's key
IV:	To release a people so cynically sold.

Scene II: Governor's offices, Vaucouleurs, February, 1429.

GOVERNOR: You again? The mad maiden from Domremy. What do you want this time?

JOAN: The same as before . . . your help in getting me to see the dauphin.

GOVERNOR: Didn't I send you home to be thrashed for such nonsense? Maybe I should have used one of my own men for the job. Now get out before I have you thrown out by your ears!

BERTRAND: Baudricourt, just listen to her. I really believe her intentions are noble. She is without guile or deceit.

GOVERNOR: This illiterate peasant? She can only tell me village drivel and teenage fantasies.

JOAN: The cause of our beloved France is grave. Our forces have just lost a great battle.

GOVERNOR: Teenage girls know nothing of military affairs. Now quickly leave, and never return!

Scene III: Peasant cottage, Vaucouleurs, days later.

JOAN: Why have you come . . . disturbing my good hosts' sleep? And with a priest as well?

GOVERNOR: I want him to determine your spiritual state.

JOAN: What difference does that make to you?

GOVERNOR: The last time we met, you told of a disastrous battle. You were correct, and now Orléans faces great danger.

JOAN: And you think only a witch or a sorceress would have known such things?

GOVERNOR: Right now, I don't know what I think. But if the priest is convinced of your purity, I'll send you to the dauphin. It will be a most difficult and dangerous journey.

20 Exciting Plays for Medieval History Classes

JOAN:	What do you mean? God is with me.
GOVERNOR:	Maybe so. But you will travel through enemy-held territory, and therefore, only at night. Are you prepared to cross icy rivers in the dark?
JOAN:	For God, and France, I will do anything.
GOVERNOR:	I'll give you a small armed escort. Somehow, I'll get word to my people in Chinon of your possible arrival. If you make it that far . . . you're on your own.

Scene IV: Royal castle, Chinon, March, 1429.

CHARLES:	Who is this maiden the whole court is buzzing about?
TREMOILLE:	Some hysterical teenager playing upon the superstitious peasantry.
CHARLES:	Then why are the nobles so excited?
REGNAULT:	The girl is like a shooting star. She dazzles for a brief moment, then burns back to oblivion.
CHARLES:	Why is she so insistent about seeing me?
TREMOILLE:	She claims voices command her.
CHARLES:	To do what!
REGNAULT:	An utterly preposterous notion . . . to escort you to Reims for your proper coronation.
CHARLES:	Anything else she's supposed to do?
TREMOILLE:	Yes . . . get you to help her raise an army to rescue Orléans.
CHARLES:	For a lowly peasant, she thinks big! Now, what should we do about her?
TREMOILLE:	Ignore her, or she could drag you into great danger . . . English and Burgundian troops control everything in and around Reims.

CHARLES: Come, come now . . . that's not being very sporting. How about quickening this shooting star's fall? I'll disguise myself amidst the court, and you challenge her to identify me. That should prove an embarrassing test of her divine mission!

CHORUS:

I:	Up in the castle, and in the great hall,
II:	Three hundred blue bloods grazed to be seen,
III:	Dressed, save the servants, for the fanciest ball—
IV:	No way a stranger could pick out the dauphin!
I:	She had to choose, or be cast aside
II:	And spurned by the king who had yet to be crowned.
III:	But once again her voices would guide,
IV:	And the hiding Charles was quickly found.
I:	Awestruck, the king met the maiden alone,
II:	And Joan revealed his severe destiny,
III:	And told him she'd save beleaguered Orléans,
IV:	If only he'd give her a true army.
I:	While Orléans suffered, Charles frittered away
II:	Time, with the pleasures of court,
III:	Hostage to men whose treason held sway,
IV:	Keeping Joan idle in his amusement fort.
I:	Finally, the call, and to Blois she was sent,
II:	Where her army was supposedly ready.
III:	But when she arrived, all order was spent,
IV:	Leaving troops unfit but for riot and comedy.

Scene V: Army camp, Blois, April, 1429.

ALENÇON: There . . . there is the "new" army.

BERTRAND: Joan, dear Joan, they're a miserable lot.

20 Exciting Plays for Medieval History Classes

ALENÇON:	They want nothing to do with discipline or training.
BERTRAND:	The only thing you hear from them are profane curses. They only move for drunken orgies.
ALENÇON:	Corrupted and compromised like the rest of the country. They'll never rescue Orléans.
BERTRAND:	If Orléans falls, everything south of the Loire River will be in great peril.
ALENÇON:	It will be the end of France.
JOAN:	I've heard enough. Call all the captains to meet me here at once.

Scene VI: A short time later.

LA HIRE:	Who in the name of the bloody saints is this dame? Oh... I forgot...the dauphin's secret weapon. Love your haircut, lady—just like the guys'.
BERTRAND:	Hey, soldier! Show some respect!
LA HIRE:	Blow it out your ear, gallant knighty! Boys, we might as well go home now... better live English dogs than dead French frogs! Ha!
JOAN:	Who is this man?
BERTRAND:	La Hire, he's called. Very unruly.
ALENÇON:	But tough as old leather and strong as steel.
JOAN:	Captain La Hire, do you love France?
LA HIRE:	What do you mean? Of course I do!
JOAN:	Do you know what will happen if the English capture Orléans?
LA HIRE:	The French cause will be hopeless.
JOAN:	Can we save Orléans?
LA HIRE:	Only with an army brave and true.

JOAN:	Like this one?
LA HIRE:	Ridiculous! Of course not!
JOAN:	One like the English army at Agincourt fourteen years ago?
BERTRAND:	Outnumbered five to one, they still defeated us.
JOAN:	Why? Why, Captain La Hire? How could they do that? Were they taller, stronger, or better armed?
LA HIRE:	I...I don't know.
JOAN:	Well, then, I'll tell you. They weren't!
LA HIRE:	What was different about the English troops, then?
JOAN:	They were disciplined! They were right with God, lean of body, sober of mind, obedient to their superiors, and united in spirit.
LA HIRE:	You...you are like that. I see clearly now what you want from me and the other captains.
JOAN:	Seeing and doing aren't the same thing.
LA HIRE:	You can count on me and my troops!
JOAN:	Good. Now we must convince all the others.
BERTRAND:	Joan, I think I'm going to like this old bear!

CHORUS:

I:	On to Orléans, in her armor of white,
II:	Where the English were well-fortified;
III:	Six months of siege, with victory in sight,
IV:	Hope was ebbing from the weary French side.
I:	Crossing the Loire, she entered the town,
II:	Raising the spirits of all,
III:	Dispensing food to all around,
IV:	She chased the cloud of Orléans' fall.

20 Exciting Plays for Medieval History Classes

I:	Then she called to the English beyond:
II:	"Leave! For your cause is not right!"
III:	They hurled back crude curses upon
IV:	Her virtue, and ability to fight.

I:	Bravely she held her battle banner high
II:	Through arrow storms raining down;
III:	When shot in the shoulder, she would lie
IV:	Bleeding victory's life on the ground.

I:	Her banner now down, her forces lost heart,
II:	And pulled back fast to the rear;
III:	But rising again, Joan roused a fresh start
IV:	To the cause so precious and dear.

I:	Now the French began to fight
II:	With frightful energy;
III:	Soon the English were put to flight,
IV:	Leaving Orléans once again free.

Scene VII: Palace, Tours, late May, 1429.

CHARLES:	You're my advisors, now what am I to do?
TREMOILLE:	I still say, ignore her. It's much too dangerous to try and reach Reims.
CHARLES:	How in the world can I ignore her! She's now the great heroine of France...the "Maid of Orléans."
REGNAULT:	Patience. In time, enthusiasm for Joan will subside...but only if you show you're in control.
TREMOILLE:	Precisely. Do not react to her, else her star will rise higher than yours. Make her react to you!
	(Enter JOAN.)
JOAN:	Dauphin, you must now go to Reims to be crowned. Your people are anxiously waiting.

CHARLES: I know . . . but the pathway must first be made safe.

JOAN: What do you mean?

CHARLES: Three enemy-controlled villages are along the way. I dare not move until Jargeau, Meung, and Beaugency are in friendly hands.

JOAN: As God is my commander, the road to Reims will soon be ours.

CHARLES: At which time, I will leave for my coronation.

CHORUS:

I: Jargeau fell, in a hot quick fight;

II: Meung was neatly cut aside.

III: Beaugency surrendered in the night,

IV: For the English had fled to hide.

I: They sought the hedges of nearby Patay

II: To launch their ambushing schemes.

III: But their battle plans proved child's play,

IV: And the road was secured to Reims.

I: When the great day finally came

II: And the king was properly crowned,

III: "Mission complete," now Joan could claim—

IV: Except the English were still around.

I: "Hunt them down like a fattened goose!"

II: Was the cry in the ranks that hour;

III: But treachery at court, in a secret truce,

IV: Let the enemy regain its power.

I: So Paris remained in foreign hands,

II: Her defenses too strong and secure;

III: And Joan's good fortunes, like sifting sands,

IV: Were now no more to be sure.

I:	Wounded painfully in the thigh,
II:	She retired from the Paris gate;
III:	Her army disbanded by and by,
IV:	The king indifferent to her fate.

I:	Pleasures of court consumed his soul,
II:	He cared not Compiègne's fate was grave;
III:	But Joan held fast to her noble goal,
IV:	Sallying forth, her people to save.

Scene VIII: Palace, Tours, June, 1430.

TREMOILLE: Joan has been captured.

REGNAULT: By the Burgundians?

TREMOILLE: Yes. She's at the castle of Jean de Luxembourg.

REGNAULT: A pity.

TREMOILLE: You're not shedding any tears.

REGNAULT: And why should I? She's completely upset the proper procedures of the Church. Her "visions" and "voices" only cloak an unbridled will.

TREMOILLE: And a threat to your ecclesiastical authority.

REGNAULT: I must perform my duty, and protect my divine office. Say . . . this plays well into your hands, too.

TREMOILLE: What are you talking about?

REGNAULT: Come, come now. The Burgundians have been paying you quite well, haven't they? And it takes a lot to keep up your widening girth.

TREMOILLE: Well, you don't look like you're just eating Communion bread either. So let's both end this joust. I serve my king with as much integrity as you serve your church. Enough said?

REGNAULT:	Enough said. Now, what should we do?
TREMOILLE:	The king will certainly hear many pleas to have Joan ransomed. We cannot let that happen.
REGNAULT:	What then?
TREMOILLE:	Luxembourg will sell Joan to the English. There's already talk that the duke of Bedford is raising the money by a special tax in Normandy.
REGNAULT:	Will he have her executed right away?
TREMOILLE:	Of course not! He'll want her first tried as a heretic.
REGNAULT:	Why would the English regent do that?
TREMOILLE:	To discredit Joan in the eyes of the people. By making her out to be a witch, he also puts a shadow over the dauphin's coronation at Reims.
REGNAULT:	And thereby makes the English claim to the throne seem more legitimate. Right?
TREMOILLE:	Right. The duke is already making plans to crown young Henry at Rouen.
REGNAULT:	If Joan is put on trial for heresy, who will try her? I'm the archbishop.
TREMOILLE:	But Rouen isn't your jurisdiction. The University of Paris is itching to get at Joan.
REGNAULT:	Burgundian-controlled to the core. Who will they get to prosecute?
TREMOILLE:	Cauchon, I believe. He hates Joan with a passion since she caused his exile. Besides, if he does well, he'll be certain to get a high church position.
REGNAULT:	What sentence will he seek? Prison? Banishment?
TREMOILLE:	What witches always get.
REGNAULT:	Then she'll be forgotten forever.

CHORUS:

I:	Sold to the English, abandoned by her king,
II:	A mockery of justice began.
III:	Denied even counsel, or fair aid to bring;
IV:	Not a sole witness friendly to her stand.
I:	Alone she faced, in this cauldron of sixty,
II:	Judges learned and wise
III:	Who rained on her, with little pity,
IV:	Absurdities and lies.
I:	But Joan was far from silent—
II:	She volleyed back each question and charge;
III:	This was no mere mindless peasant,
IV:	But a wit, well-honed and hard.
I:	Long held by men of mean contempt,
II:	Her strength kept slipping away;
III:	Confused, not knowing the true intent,
IV:	She crossed a confession one bleak day.
I:	She expected freedom from the English vile,
II:	To a church ward chainless, humane;
III:	Instead they resumed her final trial,
IV:	And returned her to that hell-cell same.
I:	She was tricked into wearing forbidden attire,
II:	And steeled to once more defy;
III:	"Recantation thus voided, she was a liar!"
IV:	And therefore, "Joan must die!"
I:	So treachery triumphed and gathered its sticks,
II:	To mete out justice with no restraint.
III:	"Look up now, they're burning a witch!"
IV:	"No," sighed an Englishman. "A saint."

Epilogue

I:	Savior of an Orléans dying,
II:	Sentry's conscience of a nation torn,
III:	Her life and death, ever inspiring,
IV:	Her ashes the seeds of a France reborn.

20 Exciting Plays for Medieval History Classes

Gutenberg and His Movable Printing Type

Characters

CHORUS I and **II**   **FUST**, investor
FELIX, goldsmith   **OZIO**, churchman
JOHANN (Gutenberg), inventor

Prologue

CHORUS:

I:	Can you imagine a time
II:	When books were rare and few;
I:	No magazines of any kind
II:	To deliver current events to you?
I:	Before the birth of movable type,
II:	Reading was limited and rare;
I:	Knowledge was kept from the people's sight,
II:	And news was an oral affair.
I:	So progress moved at a snail's rate,
II:	Because people's horizons were slight;
I:	Their freedom was left to a future date,
II:	When the printed word proved its might.
I:	In fourteen hundred was born a lad
II:	Who'd change forever our world;
I:	He was no conqueror, battle-clad,
II:	But a catalyst of learning unfurled.

I:	He developed movable type
II:	With a press that moved with speed,
I:	And oil-based ink just right,
II:	For printing clear, all words to read.
I:	The task was long and tedious,
II:	But our hero never forsook;
I:	He was poor, but his dream was serious:
II:	To mass-produce the Good Book.

Scene I: Goldsmith's shop, Strasbourg, Germany, 1439.

FELIX: Johann, is that mold ready yet?

JOHANN: Almost . . . just be patient.

FELIX: Patient? This is for our best account. Hey, are you tinkering again?

JOHANN: Here's the mold, ready for the pouring.

FELIX: Good . . . steady, steady. Done. While it cools, answer me straight, are you tinkering again?

JOHANN: Well . . . yes.

FELIX: What are you trying to make? I have a right to know.

JOHANN: A way to improve printing.

FELIX: Why? You're a goldsmith. Besides, what's there to improve? Woodblocks seem to work just fine.

JOHANN: No, they don't. Each page must have its own separate block, and they take forever to make. And if it's not carved perfectly . . . well, you either start all over or print the error.

FELIX: So then, what are you trying to do?

JOHANN: Make a metal type piece for each letter.

FELIX: That's an improvement? Ha! What a waste of time.

JOHANN: You don't understand. I'll set the letters into words held by a shank. There will be one shank for each line of a page. I'll be able to move letters about quite rapidly.

FELIX: How are you going to make sure the shank holds the letters firmly so they don't fall out or slip? And how are you going to make the letters the right size?

JOHANN: That's what I've been tinkering with. . . .

FELIX: And how are you going to make the molds for the letters? That won't be easy.

JOHANN: I know . . . but once I get that right, I'll be able to make hundreds of individual letters, all at my disposal for quickly moving about in setting a page.

FELIX: But with all that heavy metal, the pressing will surely destroy your paper.

JOHANN: I've anticipated that problem. Right now I'm working on a press that will print firmly and quickly, yet not damage the paper.

FELIX: Who could read the results? No ink can stand up to those conditions. You'll have nothing but blobs and blotches.

JOHANN: I'm working on that, too.

FELIX: Well, it seems to me you have a lot of bugs to work out—too many if you ask me. In the meantime, drop this hare-brained project and concentrate on your work here! You've bitten off more than you can chew, so spit it out before you choke on it!

Scene II: Gutenberg's workshop, Mainz, Germany, 1450.

FUST: So, Mr. Gutenberg, this is your new invention?

JOHANN: It's hardly that, Mr. Fust. I've been working on the whole process of printing for years. The machine is almost ready. I just need a little more time.

FUST: And capital . . . correct?

20 Exciting Plays for Medieval History Classes

JOHANN:	Yes, Mr. Fust. There've been some very necessary but unforeseen expenses in completing the press.
FUST:	I understand. How much of a loan do you need?
JOHANN:	Eight hundred guilders.
FUST:	Done...if you have some reasonable collateral.
JOHANN:	I...all I have is the printing press.
FUST:	Are you confident it will soon be working and turning a steady profit?
JOHANN:	I'm not sure. New inventions have their own timetables. It's unwise to rush them, or take shortcuts.
FUST:	Very well. Mr. Gutenberg, I'm a very patient man, but also a businessman. I believe your printing press has commercial potential, and therefore I'm willing to finance its development. But I won't be just an ordinary lender. I'll come in as your partner. Agreed?
JOHANN:	Your conditions?
FUST:	A full return on my original investment within five years.
JOHANN:	Agreed.
FUST:	Good. I'll have the necessary legal papers drawn up.

Scene III: Gutenberg's workshop, Mainz, Germany, 1454.

OZIO:	Mr. Gutenberg, your bid was the lowest. You get the contract.
JOHANN:	Thank you. You'll have all your documents and the number of copies you want by week's end.
OZIO:	That's a lot of work for so short a time. Can you really do it?
JOHANN:	I promise all the work will be done neatly, accurately, and on time.

OZIO:	This is very important church business. The Turks have captured Constantinople. Money is urgently needed for a new crusade. That's why I'm here—to prepare Mainz for the new sale of indulgences. That's what you'll be copying.
JOHANN:	You won't be disappointed. Come back Saturday.
OZIO:	Your shop seems so small, and I see so few workers.
JOHANN:	Trust me, the work will be done! Now . . . you're a priest, so show some faith, and let me get started!
OZIO:	Yes. Good day, Mr. Gutenberg.

Scene IV: A few days later.

JOHANN:	Ah, right on time. Your order is finished.
OZIO:	All those copies?
JOHANN:	Of course. You can count and examine them yourself.
OZIO:	They're all so neat and clear . . . and alike! How could one hand do them all?
JOHANN:	I did.
OZIO:	Impossible! You would have needed twenty hands, working day and night, to copy all this. Why do you seek to deceive me?
JOHANN:	I'm not, believe me! Let me show you something new—my printing press. Watch as I work it.
OZIO:	Amazing! Did you have twenty men carve all the woodblocks?
JOHANN:	Woodblocks are antiques! I used my movable metal type. Watch how fast I can set one sentence.
OZIO:	Can you do this for an entire page?
JOHANN:	Of course. I have plenty of shanks and letters.
OZIO:	Do you realize what your press and movable type process will do?

20 Exciting Plays for Medieval History Classes

JOHANN: Yes . . . I can finally realize my dream of printing many Bibles.

OZIO: Of course! And so very much more! Books and other printed materials will no longer be so costly. And since the average person can afford them, people by the thousands will want to learn to read.

JOHANN: I just want to get Bibles into the hands of the people—as many as I possibly can.

OZIO: I'm sure this press will do just that. And think of the books of science, philosophy, literature. . . .

JOHANN: Not literature. Who knows Latin but you priests?

OZIO: That's right! Big changes are coming! People will start writing in the language of the people. But I don't think everyone is going to welcome your invention.

JOHANN: What do you mean? Who might resist it?

OZIO: Copyists, for certain. They'll be out of work, all replaced by your machine.

JOHANN: They'll just have to get new jobs . . . in printing.

OZIO: The priests won't like your press either.

JOHANN: Why? I'll print Bibles, religious tracts—

OZIO: Fine, but what will they think when you start printing works of science, philosophy, literature, and even politics!

JOHANN: What are you driving at?

OZIO: Once books like that are printed and distributed about, the priests' monopoly on learning will cease.

JOHANN: I don't understand.

OZIO: When people have access to all kinds of books, new ideas will be planted. People will be able to think for themselves, teach themselves, and even entertain themselves.

JOHANN: Is something wrong with that?

20 Exciting Plays for Medieval History Classes

OZIO:	Right or wrong, it makes no difference. The books will be serious competition for the Church. Today, the Church controls education and thought. The future? Well, the Church will have great cause for concern.
JOHANN:	Change always seems to bring pain to someone.
OZIO:	And your machine will bring many and great changes. Thank you, Mr. Gutenberg, for your excellent work.

Scene V: Gutenberg's workshop, Mainz, Germany, 1455.

JOHANN:	Mr. Fust, how are you this fine day?
FUST:	Our partnership is dissolved. Here are all the proper documents.
JOHANN:	But . . . but why?
FUST:	I gave you five years to pay back my investment. Did you? No. I even gave you another eight hundred guilders.
JOHANN:	The Bible is a very long book. It takes lots of time. . . .
FUST:	You should have been working on projects that return quicker profits!
JOHANN:	I have!
FUST:	But not enough to keep this business in the black.
JOHANN:	What are you going to do now?
FUST:	What the law and our original contract say I'm entitled to do. The printing press is now mine, one hundred percent. I'll use it as I please.
JOHANN:	But . . . my Bibles!
FUST:	Finish them on another press.
JOHANN:	Don't mock me. You know very well this is the only one of its kind.
FUST:	Then you'll just have to make another one . . . but with someone else's money this time.

Epilogue

CHORUS:

I: Gutenberg's great development

II: Of printing words with ease

I: Would launch the European continent

II: As first catcher of each changing breeze.

I: Each changing breeze of fashion,

II: In the fine arts, and all things new,

I: Building and navigation,

II: And a scientific point of view.

I: For centuries Gutenberg's contribution

II: Was hidden from history's eyes;

I: Though others falsely claimed the distinction,

II: His gift is now fully realized.

20 Exciting Plays for Medieval History Classes

Isabella and the Rise of Unified Spain

Characters

CHORUS I, II, III, IV
MOTHER (of Isabella)
ISABELLA
HENRY, the king of Castile
MARIA, Isabella's confidante

JUAN, Isabella's confessor
FERDINAND of Aragon
COLUMBUS
LUIS, Ferdinand's finance minister

Prologue

CHORUS:

I:	Spain, Spain, glorious Spain,
II:	Language and culture spread far,
III:	Forged to greatness under Isabella's reign,
IV:	With husband for king and co-star.
I:	Before their rule, you were just a name,
II:	Torn by tribe and religion;
III:	Your king, a man of dissolute fame,
IV:	Only fed your chaos and division.
I:	Your land divided by a jealous four,
II:	Navarre, Aragon, and Castile,
III:	Moorish Granada behind Islam's door,
IV:	Made a unified Spain a dream unreal.
I:	Yet dreams are not chased in the deep-rutted way,
II:	But in detours through thickets and sand,
III:	Where perseverance and skill hold sway,
IV:	Bring forth each purpose grand.

I:	For Isabella, of upright soul,
II:	A righteous Spain, strong and unified,
III:	Was her passion and consuming goal,
IV:	Pursued relentlessly until she died.

I:	Not only Spain would she look upon
II:	To spread her culture and Catholic creed,
III:	But to new lands, vast oceans beyond,
IV:	Her inspired vision did eagerly feed.

Scene I: Arevalo, Castile (Spain), c. 1460.

MOTHER:	Dear daughter, I have something very important to discuss with you.
ISABELLA:	Yes, Mother.
MOTHER:	You know I have tried to give you the best education, a firm foundation in morals and Catholic belief.
ISABELLA:	You have prepared me well, and I am grateful.
MOTHER:	Do you realize I've been preparing you to be queen?
ISABELLA:	Queen? But my half-brother is not old. Besides, won't he want his own child to succeed him?
MOTHER:	Henry has the morals of a mongrel dog. His court moves about like a caravan of pigs. But the stench always stays, ruining our country. The leading families have had enough of him. They want you!
ISABELLA:	But what about my younger brother?
MOTHER:	He is frail, and you are strong. You are the one most fit to bring glory and honor to Spain.
ISABELLA:	But I am only nine...so many things can happen.
MOTHER:	Your time will come. God will protect you...if you honor and protect His holy church.

Scene II: Royal court,
Castile, 1467.

HENRY: Isabella, I have arranged for your marriage to Don Pedro Giron. The wedding preparations are nearly complete.

ISABELLA: Call them off! I'll never marry that old goat. Why . . . he's as degenerate as you are!

HENRY: Just as I thought . . . your priest tutors have made you too prissy and uppity. That's why I had you brought here, away from those stuffy and long-faced blue noses. I'm the king, and you'll do your duty!

ISABELLA: I'll do my duty . . . as God commands.

HENRY: This marriage will solve many political problems.

ISABELLA: You're not listening. I will not be your pawn!

HENRY: Don Pedro will arrive within a week.

ISABELLA: Over my dead body will he be my husband!

CHORUS:

I:	Providence shone on Isabella's strong will,
II:	For Don Pedro died soon after;
III:	For his role, so historic to fill,
IV:	She opened Spain's greatest chapter.
I:	From Aragon she chose her mate,
II:	A soldier tried and true,
III:	Bringing as dowry a future fate:
IV:	A nation strong and unified anew.
I:	Ferdinand was handsome, bold, and strong,
II:	In politics, quick and agile,
III:	Keen to good fortune, short and long,
IV:	Single-minded, and very resourceful.

20 Exciting Plays for Medieval History Classes

Scene III: Segovia, Castile, December 11, 1474.

MARIA:	My lady, why is King Henry so mean to you?
ISABELLA:	You mean his refusal to give me my rightful royal income?
MARIA:	Yes. You and your husband live like poor peasants.
ISABELLA:	That will change, in God's good time. Henry hates me because I stood up to him, and wouldn't marry so-and-so to further his political fortunes.
MARIA:	Why did you choose Ferdinand of Aragon?
ISABELLA:	To unite Spain's greatest kingdoms, Castile and Aragon. Someday, when I am queen and Ferdinand is king, we will make Spain truly Spain.
MARIA:	Do you really love Ferdinand?
ISABELLA:	I do. We are very well suited, and I am completely devoted to him.
MARIA:	But he seems so restless.
ISABELLA:	Because he's still just the heir to the throne in Aragon.
MARIA:	Isn't he there now?
ISABELLA:	Yes...helping out his father again. There's always some insurrection brewing in Aragon.
MARIA:	Just like in Castile.
ISABELLA:	Unfortunately, yes. But things will change...these divisions and feuds will end. Justice and order will return to Spain.
	(Enter JUAN PEREZ.)
JUAN:	Momentous news...King Henry is dead!
MARIA:	At last, you will be queen.
ISABELLA:	Pray for my half-brother's soul. Inform the council. I want my coronation within two days.

20 Exciting Plays for Medieval History Classes

Scene IV: Queen's household, Segovia, days later.

ISABELLA: Ferdinand, dear Ferdinand, welcome back. I trust those problems are resolved.

FERDINAND: In Aragon, yes, for the time being . . . but not for me in Castile.

ISABELLA: What do you mean? I'm now the queen.

FERDINAND: I read the council's document of succession.

ISABELLA: A mere formality.

FERDINAND: It states that you, and you alone, are the sole monarch of Castile. Why, I can't even legally leave Castile without your permission.

ISABELLA: These conditions aren't new. They are all part of our original marriage contract.

FERDINAND: But . . . I thought . . . I hoped that when this time finally came, you would make me king, or at least declare me as the rightful heir.

ISABELLA: And if I did that, my days as queen would end. Anarchy would return to Castile. Don't you understand? The support I now enjoy from the people and the council must not be jeopardized. Be patient, and cultivate their support yourself.

FERDINAND: Then what is my role here, besides husband?

ISABELLA: We share the same goals, and we will rule together. Don't be concerned about titles on fancy parchment. You have my trust . . . and only that really matters. Now, where should we begin?

FERDINAND: Law and order must be secured throughout the realm. Bandits are everywhere.

ISABELLA: We'll form an incorruptible national police force.

FERDINAND: To administer justice, fairly and completely.

ISABELLA: We'll codify the laws—

20 Exciting Plays for Medieval History Classes

FERDINAND:	So all citizens will understand and respect them.
ISABELLA:	We'll reduce the power of the nobles.
FERDINAND:	Yes. Take control of their military societies, and end their powers of coining money.
ISABELLA:	We'll promote trade.
FERDINAND:	Yes, by building more roads and bridges.
ISABELLA:	And controlling the money supply.
FERDINAND:	And getting rid of old laws that hinder new commerce and industry.
ISABELLA:	We'll promote and strengthen our royal authority.
FERDINAND:	Always and evermore...but that won't be easy.
ISABELLA:	I know, but these reforms will help. Also, we must be more accessible to the common people.
FERDINAND:	Knocking the nobles down and raising up the people... now that's a winning strategy to strengthen our royal cause. Castile will never be the same.
ISABELLA:	And when you become king of Aragon...neither will Spain.

CHORUS:

I:	Spain's road to glory was long and steep—
II:	Foreign enemies were poised and ready,
III:	Potholes of factions were many and deep—
IV:	A dead end but to the strong and steady.

I:	The strong and steady hands of state
II:	That led a nation-to-be,
III:	Crushing all foes, small and great,
IV:	That challenged the course to unity.

20 Exciting Plays for Medieval History Classes

I:	Portugal's king pressed a dubious claim,
II:	Contesting Isabella's crown,
III:	Invading Castile, his treachery so plain,
IV:	Her power and rule to bring down.

I:	But the wedded two were up to the task,
II:	The queen inspired her people;
III:	Ferdinand's troops performed as asked,
IV:	Insuring the victory full.

I:	With the Portuguese threat eliminated,
II:	Royal power and authority increased,
III:	When in Aragon, finally coronated,
IV:	Ferdinand's ambitions were released.

I:	Spain's curse was chaos, unity the goal,
II:	So the monarchs set into position
III:	The chains to keep non-conformists in tow:
IV:	The Spanish Inquisition.

I:	Orthodoxy was their stick
II:	That measured clear each deviant's guilt;
III:	Secretly accused, arrest was quick—
IV:	No public defense allowed to be built.

I:	Many suffered, especially the Jews
II:	Who claimed they were converted;
III:	But the Inquisition only tightened its screws
IV:	With measures mean and perverted.

I:	With the quest for amalgamation keen,
II:	Relations with Granada grew tense;
III:	Islam's last stronghold in Spain was seen
IV:	As a political boil and cultural offense.

20 Exciting Plays for Medieval History Classes

I:	The fighting was filled with unbridled fury,
II:	Slash and siege were Ferdinand's allies;
III:	As the Moors grew famished and war-weary,
IV:	They surrendered their seven-centuries-held prize.

Scene V: Santa Fe (siege city before Granada), January 2, 1492.

FERDINAND: The great moment is near. The Moorish leaders will soon make their final exit.

ISABELLA: Your terms of surrender were most generous.

FERDINAND: And prudent. We achieved our greatest desire without wasting any more blood or resources.

ISABELLA: Your tactics were brilliant: destroy their food supplies and pound their forts with great siege guns.

FERDINAND: You're the one most responsible for our artillery. You had the foresight to bring in craftsmen from France, Italy, and Germany to make the guns. And you raised the money to pay for them.

ISABELLA: No effort was too great for our cause. You, not I, led our brave troops in battle.

FERDINAND: But you made them an army. Your presence inspired them when they were weary and discouraged. Your example of purity made them disciplined.

ISABELLA: They have given so much for Spain. . . .

FERDINAND: As you have given for their welfare—the food, clothes, and hospitals you provided for them raised their spirits, so they were willing to fight on to final victory.

(Exit FERDINAND, enter JUAN.)

JUAN: My queen, Christopher Columbus has arrived.

ISABELLA: Timely for him . . . he'll witness history with the Moors' surrender. Let him in.

(Enter COLUMBUS.)

COLUMBUS:	Queen Isabella, I congratulate you on your great victory.
ISABELLA:	It has been a long ordeal.
COLUMBUS:	You of course realize the Turks control the old land routes to the Orient.
ISABELLA:	And our holy places.
COLUMBUS:	I've carefully worked out a plan for reaching China by sailing west. All I need are a few ships and sailors. My own resources are limited.
ISABELLA:	And mine have been drained by this war. I will consult my advisers.
COLUMBUS:	Again? You did that before, and I was turned down. I'll go to the French, then.

(Exit COLUMBUS.)

ISABELLA:	Juan, go find Luis de Santander, Ferdinand's finance minister.
JUAN:	The baptized Jew? For what purpose?
ISABELLA:	I need wiser counsel about Columbus.

(JUAN exits, returns with LUIS.)

LUIS:	You sent for me, Queen Isabella.
ISABELLA:	I need your advice about Columbus and his plan.
LUIS:	Give him what he needs for his voyage.
ISABELLA:	But the treasury is empty!
LUIS:	Where is Columbus now?
JUAN:	On the road to France.
LUIS:	You are letting him go to the French?
ISABELLA:	What else could I do?

LUIS:	You've been too concerned with the cost. Think of the reward! All of Asia would be open to Christianity, thanks to you.
ISABELLA:	Yes, yes! I had only been thinking about trade—spices, silk....
LUIS:	Imagine, you, Queen Isabella, bringing a whole continent into the arms of the Holy Catholic Church!
ISABELLA:	I will find the money! I'll pledge my own jewels for this venture.
LUIS:	That's not necessary. I can raise the needed funds from my fraternity.
ISABELLA:	What fraternity?
JUAN:	Of converted Jews.
LUIS:	Of people with vision and enterprise.
ISABELLA:	Then it's done. Juan, quickly find Columbus and bring him back here. Luis, thank you for your counsel and support.
LUIS:	I will make the necessary arrangements.

CHORUS:

I:	Off to the Orient Columbus did sail,
II:	Little thinking by destiny now hurled,
III:	Into a pioneer's ocean trail,
IV:	Bravely he entered the new world.
I:	Many would follow in his wake—
II:	Schemers and saints, the cruel and the kind—
III:	From the Americas Spain would take
IV:	Vast wealth, and leave her culture behind.
I:	For Spain, this great addition
II:	In the tally sheet of time

20 Exciting Plays for Medieval History Classes

III:	Was debased by the Inquisition
IV:	With a melancholy crime.
I:	First the Jews, and then the Moors
II:	Were exiled to purify Spain,
III:	Leaving behind bigotry's doors
IV:	An empire ascending while drained.
I:	Drained of its talents, in industry, finance,
II:	Her mind-set remained medieval;
III:	Phobic of freedoms that would enhance
IV:	A greatness unequivocal.

Leonardo da Vinci
(1452–1519)

Characters

CHORUS I, II, III, IV   **MATTEO**, observer, writer
PETER, village priest   **TESSA**, **GINA**, **DOMINIC**, and
LEONARDO   **CESARE**, Florentine citizens
ANDREA (Verrocchio), artist

Prologue

CHORUS:

I:	Some say the mind of each human
II:	Is bound by one's times and genes,
III:	And all that's new, under the sun,
IV:	Are costumes in revolving scenes.
I:	Yet stealing upon the great stage
II:	Of history plotted straight,
III:	Come those bringing their own page,
IV:	Redirecting the drama's fate.
I:	Scripts of conquest by the hand,
II:	Technologies of every kind,
III:	Deeds and words, new and grand,
IV:	From the mysteries of the mind.
I:	No mind was ever so broad or keen
II:	In the annals of history;
III:	A passion to know all he'd seen,
IV:	Beyond . . . within . . . Leonardo da Vinci.

Scene I: Tuscan countryside, Italy, c. 1462.

PETER: Leonardo! What are you doing down there?

LEONARDO: Catching butterflies. Aren't they beautiful?

PETER: Yes, but how do you catch them in such perfect form?

LEONARDO: With my trap-box.

PETER: Interesting design. What's this device?

LEONARDO: A pulley. It controls the tension on the line holding the trap door. That way I don't hurt the captured butterfly when I close the trap.

PETER: I see. Leonardo, I seldom see you in church. Your father tells me you're always out here.

LEONARDO: I love looking at the flowers, animals, water, sky. . . .

PETER: You love looking at everything in nature.

LEONARDO: Yes. I want to learn . . . learn why the plants are green, how the butterflies and birds fly—

PETER: Our Creator does not intend man to possess such knowledge, especially ten-year-old boys!

LEONARDO: He intends for me! Why else would He put such a burning desire in my heart and mind?

CHORUS:

I:	His painting skills were early seen,
II:	And more than in abundance;
III:	When he turned a precocious fifteen,
IV:	He left for Renaissance Florence.

I:	There, under the kind Verrocchio,
II:	He mastered the painting craft;
III:	And the challenges of the studio
IV:	Climaxed in one unique draft.

Scene II: Verrocchio's studio, Florence, c. 1470.

ANDREA: Leonardo, you're my only left-handed student?

LEONARDO: I think so.

ANDREA: Fine. I want you to paint an angel in the left corner of one of my works.

LEONARDO: What's the theme?

ANDREA: Oh, another "Baptism of Christ" scene, very common and traditional.

LEONARDO: Thank you for this assignment.

Scene III: Days later.

ANDREA: Can I take a look?

LEONARDO: Certainly. Is there something wrong?

ANDREA: I...I...I can't believe what I'm seeing! Leonardo, did you really do this angel?

LEONARDO: Yes, right where you asked me to.

ANDREA: How? In all my years, I've never seen anything like it. Compared to your angel, all my figures seem wooden and stiff.

LEONARDO: I'm still not sure what you're asking me.

ANDREA: Your figure draws me into the painting. The angel...it seems alive...I sense its inner emotion and feeling. How could a painter possibly do this?

LEONARDO: I use geometric lines to draw in the viewer, and outward physical movement to express the inner feeling and character of the subject.

CHORUS:

I:	Off to the north, where he earned a job—
II:	His employer, the duke of Milan—
III:	Producing pageants for the artistocrat mob,
IV:	And other fluff to smile upon.

I:	What a waste of talent, so fresh and rare!
II:	Was this his fated course?
III:	Then the duke offered his dare:
IV:	"Sculpt me a giant horse!"

I:	A horse that measured twenty-six feet tall,
II:	With bronze to weigh eighty tons;
III:	His clay model, that awed one and all,
IV:	Alas, was not cast; the duke needed guns.

Scene IV: Monastery of Santa Maria delle Grazie, Milan, 1498.

MATTEO: Master Leonardo, may I talk to you about your painting, the "Last Supper"?

LEONARDO: Certainly . . . and who are you?

MATTEO: Matteo Bandello. I hope to be a writer.

LEONARDO: A writer? I write a lot myself . . . so many notebooks I can't keep track of them all.

MATTEO: About your technique . . . even though this is a wall painting, it's not done in fresco. Why?

LEONARDO: Two reasons. First, a fresco painter must work very rapidly. I'm not suited to that style.

MATTEO: I've been watching you from afar for many weeks. I've watched you mount the scaffold before sunrise and paint without stopping till sunset. Doesn't that indicate you are suited for fresco work?

20 Exciting Plays for Medieval History Classes

LEONARDO: Mechanically, I'm capable; artistically, no. Have you seen me sit for hours before the work, and then only add a stroke or two? Have you seen me jump down, and race into the streets?

MATTEO: Yes...I must admit your work habits puzzle me. Why have you raced into the streets?

LEONARDO: Because I saw a face, a special face I needed to examine closely before I used it here.

MATTEO: I've heard the prior doesn't approve of them.

LEONARDO: I know...who does he think those twelve disciples were? I paint the faces of fishermen, carpenters, and tax collectors. Human beings like you and me...not bloodless clay saints.

MATTEO: What was your second reason for not painting a fresco?

LEONARDO: Colors. I'm experimenting with many new oil shades. I've used a special primer over the wall to accommodate them.

MATTEO: That's a radically new technique. Do you foresee any problems?

LEONARDO: Innovation, like new birth, has its risks.

MATTEO: One final question. Your "Last Supper" is unlike any other painting. The disciples seem so alive, the viewer experiences their emotions. Can you comment—

LEONARDO: I needed an emotion-filled moment to probe the depths of each figure. Imagine you were one of the twelve, and Christ says, "One of you will betray me." Can you sense the drama of that moment?

MATTEO: Like walking into a lightning bolt.

LEONARDO: Yes. That's what I've tried to capture in each of their faces and gestures.

MATTEO: Thank you so much, Master Leonardo.

LEONARDO: You're most welcome.

(MATTEO begins to exit, stops.)

20 Exciting Plays for Medieval History Classes

MATTEO: Oh...one other thing. What was that little ruckus about yesterday with some of the local street toughs? You held something up, spread your arms, and then they all seemed to scatter like frightened birds.

LEONARDO: A misunderstanding that needed clearing up. They'd been razzing me for some time about the way I dress. Every time they saw me they'd all yell, "Peacock! Peacock!" I just thought they needed to know a little more about me.

MATTEO: So you just confronted them, and waved them away?

LEONARDO: Not quite. I asked one of them to bring me a horseshoe. When I proceeded to unbend it, we all had a new understanding of each other.

CHORUS:

I: But this great work decayed to ruin;
II: The primer cracked and would not hold.
III: Even still, his genius was proven
IV: By the story his brush had told.

I: Then began an interlude queer—
II: Borgia, his patron, brutal and blunt,
III: Making new maps, a military engineer,
IV: Until the fall of this ruthless tyrant.

I: Back to Florence for engineering work
II: To alter a river's flow;
III: Then emerged a task with a quirk:
IV: Share a project with Michelangelo.

I: In the chambers of the city hall
II: Were planned two battle scenes;
III: Each was given a separate wall
IV: To glorify the victorious Florentines.

I:	Was this to be a "Renaissance show-down"?
II:	Hyped as "Two Giants in a Painter's Brush Duel"?
III:	Michelangelo of "Pieta" renown
IV:	And Leonardo, the multi-talented jewel?

Scene V: Outside City Hall, Florence, c. 1504.

TESSA: Mark my words...Michelangelo's mural will be the best!

GINA: Ridiculous! He's only a stone chiseler.

DOMINIC: That's right. Leonardo is the greatest of all painters. Have you seen his "Last Supper"?

CESARE: I have...and the paint is already starting to blister and scale.

TESSA: He was foolish for not making a fresco. The painting won't last. Michelangelo...now there's an artist equal to any challenge!

GINA: And so is Leonardo! He can do anything!

CESARE: Start, you mean, but never finish...like that horse. They left the model out so the French could use it for target practice!

DOMINIC: Was that Leonardo's fault? The stupid duke wouldn't give him the bronze. That whole project...it just wasn't possible.

TESSA: Michelangelo would have found a way.

CESARE: That's right. He took an "impossible" slab of marble...and is making out of it a giant statue of David.

TESSA: It's nearly finished—over twelve feet tall!

CESARE: And the definition of the body...it's perfect!

GINA: But it's not a painting!

DOMINIC: Our friends tell us Leonardo is working on a woman's portrait that, when finished, will never be rivaled.

20 Exciting Plays for Medieval History Classes

CESARE:	When finished...ha! We've heard that one before! Besides, these murals are scenes of war, not dainty ladies!
GINA:	Ha! A turtle in the sand has seen more battles than Michelangelo! Just remember, Leonardo knows war.

CHORUS:

I:	But alas, this drama proved hollow;
II:	Michelangelo abandoned his task,
III:	And the heart-stopping action of Leonardo
IV:	Was fated again not to last.

I:	He went to Rome, like his rival,
II:	And there he must have seen
III:	The ceiling of the Sistine Chapel,
IV:	Michelangelo's spectacle supreme.

I:	But there he gained no glory,
II:	No projects his genius to enhance;
III:	And the final chapter to his story
IV:	Was a melancholy ending, in France.

Epilogue

CHORUS:

I:	But death does not entomb greatness
II:	In one like Leonardo,
III:	And the impact of his genius
IV:	With time continues to grow.

I:	No anatomical drawings
II:	Were ever so precise and fine;
III:	And the visions of his engineering
IV:	Were generations ahead of their time.

I:	Mapmaker supreme, he charted birds,
II:	Probing the physics of flight;
III:	He wrote about art with insightful words
IV:	And every science in sight.

I:	Like an eagle ascending the heavens,
II:	His genius chased the stars;
III:	And his soaring spirit still leavens
IV:	The break-out from our horizons' bars.

20 Exciting Plays for Medieval History Classes

Martin Luther and the Protestant Reformation

<table>
<tr><td colspan="2" align="center">Characters</td></tr>
<tr>
<td>CHORUS I, II, III, IV
STAUPITZ, Luther's mentor
LUTHER, Augustinian monk, reformer
FREDA, STEPH, and HANS, German peasants</td>
<td>ECK, official of the Archbishop of Trier
CHARLES (V), Holy Roman Emperor</td>
</tr>
</table>

Prologue

CHORUS:

I:	In fourteen hundred and eighty-three,
II:	Martin Luther, in Germany, was born,
III:	But the Germans then lacked a real unity,
IV:	Except in a Church about to be torn.
I:	Times were harsh, the system mean,
II:	Especially for the working poor;
III:	Joy and ease were seldom seen,
IV:	Just suffering and death seemed sure.
I:	Discipline and obedience were the rule,
II:	In Martin's boyhood home;
III:	Fifteen floggings at a village school
IV:	He paid for one grammar question blown.

Scene I: Augustinian cloister, Erfurt, Germany, July, 1505.

STAUPITZ: My son, you're as pale as fresh snow. You must be gravely sick.

LUTHER: I...I was nearly struck by lightning up the road.

STAUPITZ: That explains why you're shaking so. Come inside and rest until your strength and nerves recover.

LUTHER: I wish to stay longer than that.

STAUPITZ: I don't understand.

LUTHER: I want to enter your order, and become a monk.

STAUPITZ: This is not a decision to be taken lightly, or when the mind and body have just experienced great stress.

LUTHER: During the storm I cried out to St. Anne for help. I vowed to be a monk if I survived.

STAUPITZ: Are you truly prepared for such a life?

LUTHER: I have two university degrees, and a determined soul. Isn't that sufficient?

STAUPITZ: Your soul—is it at peace, my son?

LUTHER: Not in my present career, a student of law.

STAUPITZ: I appreciate your honesty and candor. I'll begin the steps for your admittance.

Scene II: Augustinian cloister, Erfurt, Germany, April, 1507.

STAUPITZ: Martin, are you anxious about your upcoming ordination and first Mass?

LUTHER: I have diligently prepared myself.

STAUPITZ: Too diligently, I fear.

LUTHER:	How else can one please God?
STAUPITZ:	But you have gone too far. You fast too much, your vigils are too long, and you abase yourself by constantly confessing sins that only exist in your imagination.
LUTHER:	I only seek to please God.
STAUPITZ:	I know, I know. But there is no joy, no peace to your spirit. I worry about you, Martin.
LUTHER:	I'm always worrying about myself.
STAUPITZ:	Worrying is not the problem. It's anger.
LUTHER:	What do you mean?
STAUPITZ:	Deep down I believe you are angry with God. Why? Because you can only see and feel God as being angry with you. You need some fresh insights into the nature of God.
LUTHER:	You mean I should meditate more?
STAUPITZ:	I'm giving you your own Bible and the writings of St. Augustine. Meditate on them.

CHORUS:

I:	He studied and fasted, suffered and prayed,
II:	But found no peace, no heavenly goal;
III:	Now the monster conscience he had made
IV:	Found him deep in the night of his soul.
I:	How could he, a man who sinned,
II:	Find favor with a righteous God?
III:	With the fervor of a howling wind
IV:	He clung to despair, before Judgment's rod.
I:	Sent to Wittenberg, a tough-drinking burg,
II:	Doctor of Theology he became;
III:	He studied and taught the Holy Word,
IV:	And realized a respected name.

20 Exciting Plays for Medieval History Classes

I:	And then the fateful revelation struck
II:	Like lightning long years past:
III:	A verse from Romans forever stuck,
IV:	Healing his tortured soul at last.

I:	About God's saving, eternal grace,
II:	He no more felt anxious or deceived;
III:	Not money, not merit secured a heavenly place,
IV:	But a faith in Christ, humbly received.

Scene III: Marketplace, Wittenberg, October, 1517.

LUTHER:	Good morning, friends. Have you seen any fresh fish for sale?
FREDA:	Not yet. We haven't looked very hard since we just spent all our money.
STEPH:	Buying two special indulgences.
FREDA:	From Friar Tetzel across the river.
STEPH:	And now we'd like to know if they are real.
FREDA:	A learned professor like you, Dr. Luther, would surely know.
LUTHER:	For what purpose is the indulgence?
FREDA:	Hans, what did Friar Tetzel say?
HANS:	To raise money for the blood-sucking pope and his debauched cronies!
STEPH:	Nephew! How dare you say such things! Especially in front of a man of the church!
HANS:	My anger is not towards Dr. Luther. I respect him. It's against those pigs in Rome! They take too much of our money, and meddle too much in our own affairs!
STEPH:	I'm so ashamed. Please excuse his rashness. Like many youths, he speaks before he thinks.

LUTHER:	In truth, I think he speaks for many Germans, young and old. Now, before I examine these indulgences, what did Friar Tetzel really say?
HANS:	The money is to help rebuild St. Peter's Basilica in Rome.
LUTHER:	And you don't believe him?
HANS:	Tetzel's not lying, he's just not telling the whole truth.
LUTHER:	Do you presume to know the whole truth?
HANS:	Does anyone in these matters? But I have heard our esteemed archbishop owes the Vatican lots of money, and he's been promised a percentage of the sale.
LUTHER:	So that's why he hired the master salesman, Tetzel. A deplorable situation.
STEPH:	All I want to know is, does this indulgence release my parents from Purgatory?
FREDA:	And does mine protect me from eternal damnation?
LUTHER:	Ladies, I'm sorry to inform you, but—
HANS:	You should have saved your money to buy fish!
STEPH:	Why do you so rudely interrupt! Dr. Luther knows about these matters, not you. So shut up!
LUTHER:	The Bible teaches that only faith in Christ makes us righteous before God. Only that faith brings eternal salvation, not money, not human good works.
HANS:	I told you they were worthless.
FREDA:	I'm going back to tell that Friar Tetzel a thing or two!
LUTHER:	And I think I'll invite him to come here for a debate, so the people will learn for themselves how cynical and deceitful this indulgence sale is.
HANS:	Good man, Dr. Luther! Give that pope's rascal a hundred blows!

CHORUS:

I:	Not a hundred blows, but ninety-five,
II:	He nailed to All Saints Church door:
III:	Theses of debate, soon and live,
IV:	Calling all wits to a verbal war.

I:	But Luther's own stand was later to be,
II:	For his fire fast jumped academia's ring
III:	Into the streets for all to see,
IV:	Blown by the winds of mass printing.

I:	Now the issues grew beyond
II:	Mere issues of doctrine and belief,
III:	To challenge the Church's imperial bond
IV:	From which many Germans sought relief.

I:	As the rebellion spread across Europe's north,
II:	The Roman Church roused from its quiet;
III:	To restore authority, it called Luther forth,
IV:	To answer before the emperor's Diet.

I:	Before he appeared, he unleashed his pen,
II:	Directing the Church's reform,
III:	Proclaimed the priesthood of all women and men
IV:	Who, in faith, had been spiritually reborn.

I:	Debate retired, and gave the stage
II:	To drama, clear and bold;
III:	Now the question of the age:
IV:	Would Europe shatter its medieval mold?

Scene IV: Imperial Diet, Worms, April 17, 1521.

ECK: Martin Luther, you have been summoned to this Diet to answer but two questions. . . .

LUTHER: I don't understand. I thought this was to be a scholarly debate.

ECK: An unwise assumption. Please examine the stack of books on the table. First question, did you write them?

LUTHER: Yes.

ECK: Final question. Is there anything in them you now wish to take back, to recant?

LUTHER: I . . . I don't know. I need some time. . . .

Scene V: Evening of the next day.

ECK: Your answer?

LUTHER: Unless convinced by holy scripture, or reason, I will not take back any of my charges. I only ask to be excused for the vehemence of my words.

ECK: And not their content?

LUTHER: No, only their tone.

ECK: What! They are still naked heresy! You have subverted Church doctrine, practice, and authority. Do you . . . do you realize how far you have strayed?

LUTHER: The Church has strayed from holy scripture.

ECK: According to *your* interpretations. You know what the Bible is like . . . it's like soft wax; anyone can twist and shape it as he pleases. That's why the Church must speak with one voice on its meaning and intent.

LUTHER: I believe each individual has the right, and the duty, to read the Bible for himself.

ECK: Do you have any idea of the implications of such thinking? Of course not! For the last time, what will you recant?

LUTHER: Nothing. Here I stand. I cannot do otherwise. So help me God ... amen.

CHARLES: I've heard enough. You are excused, Martin Luther.

Scene VI: A few days later.

ECK: Emperor, your verdict?

CHARLES: Martin Luther is to be condemned. He has twenty-one days to return directly to Wittenberg under my safe conduct grant. *(Enter German soldier, carrying signs.)* What is the meaning of this ... these pictures of boots?

ECK: Emperor, they are the peasants' symbol for revolution. They see Luther as their champion.

CHARLES: Enough! The empire must be rid of this man and his subversive ideas!

CHORUS:

I:	Despairing his career, now thought at end,
II:	He left Worms with great anxiety,
III:	Rescued, then hidden, from the emperor's men,
IV:	He began a comfortable captivity.
I:	Wartburg Castle was his haven-to-be,
II:	But he was restless for something to do;
III:	With his pen he shaped German destiny:
IV:	In the people's tongue wrote the Testament New.
I:	After ten full months, he left that place
II:	To control the Reformation now begun,
III:	For chaos was running violently apace,
IV:	Hollowing the victory that principle had won.

I:	His goal had not been division,
II:	But a Church reformed, purified;
III:	To Luther it had sullied its mission,
IV:	Becoming corrupt and ossified.

I:	He taught and preached, counseled and wrote,
II:	A workload few others could carry;
III:	Then he crossed his monkish last moat:
IV:	At forty-two, he chose to marry.

I:	This former priest chose a former nun
II:	His remaining years to share;
III:	Six children blessed this unique union,
IV:	And mellowed the lion in his lair.

I:	In his final years, music became
II:	His fitting expression when awed;
III:	With ear attuned to the Heavenly Name,
IV:	He penned "A Mighty Fortress Is Our God."

I:	What is Luther's corner to be—
II:	Villain, or Protestant hero?
III:	This is sure: In the drama of history,
IV:	He scripted new lines for the individual.

Copernicus: Founder of Modern Astronomy

Characters

CHORUS I, II, III, IV
LUCAS, uncle
ANDREAS, older brother
COPERNICUS (Nicolaus)

CELTES, friend and scholar
RHETICUS, Protestant friend and scholar
GIESE, colleague and friend

Prologue

CHORUS:

I:	On a clear and star-filled night,
II:	Have you ever looked up in awe,
III:	And wondered with all your earthly might
IV:	The meaning of what you saw?
I:	Did you feel small, or grand?
II:	Did the heavens tell a story?
III:	Was this chance? Or was it planned?
IV:	Who, or what, should own this glory?
I:	Throughout all the ages,
II:	In the stars were thought revealed,
III:	By sinners and saints, fools and sages,
IV:	Mysteries to earth-bound minds concealed.
I:	Many claimed the future was told
II:	In heavenly configurations;
III:	So astrology, like soap, was sold
IV:	To countless generations.

I:	Yet a quiet few did not explore
II:	Prophecies or predictions,
III:	But a planetary system based on more
IV:	Science than superstitions.

I:	Ptolemy of Egypt said long ago,
II:	All heavenly bodies rotated
III:	Around the Earth; he calculated so
IV:	In a system most complicated.

I:	The Church proclaimed this canon fact,
II:	For it brought humanity to the center
III:	Of all creation in a solemn pact,
IV:	With pope as earthly defender.

I:	But what if Ptolemy were mistaken,
II:	And the Earth went around the sun?
III:	Would humanity feel lost and forsaken,
IV:	With its world view now undone?

I:	Or would humanity feel liberated,
II:	To run with reason wide and far,
III:	And blast the curse that all was fated
IV:	By an alignment of some star?

Scene I: Torun, Poland, c. 1483.

LUCAS:	Boys, this is a very hard time. We all need to support each other.
ANDREAS:	We never thought father would die so young.
COPERNICUS:	What's to become of us?
LUCAS:	You're all coming to live with me. I've already discussed the matter with my sister—your mother.

20 Exciting Plays for Medieval History Classes

ANDREAS:	You are so generous, Uncle Lucas.
COPERNICUS:	You've always been good to us.
LUCAS:	Isn't that why God put us on the Earth, to love and care for one another?
ANDREAS:	How could we ever repay you?
LUCAS:	By doing the same to another! You can help me a bit . . . tell me what plans you two have for the future.
ANDREAS:	I'm sure mother will ask an astrologer.
LUCAS:	Your mother is a wonderful person, but don't give a moment's ear to that nonsense! So, what's it to be? *You* choose, not the stars.
ANDREAS:	I very much want to attend the university.
LUCAS:	Excellent! I'll help you all I can. And, you, Nicolaus . . . I know you're only ten, but it's never too early to plan. What interests you?
COPERNICUS:	So many, many things. I want to serve God—
LUCAS:	A career in the church? I have good connections.
COPERNICUS:	I want to help those who are sick and hurt—
LUCAS:	A doctor . . . most admirable. These are very noble and serious pursuits. But, tell me, what activity is most fun for you?
COPERNICUS:	I love looking at the stars.
LUCAS:	And so do I . . . but not for the reasons astrologers do.
ANDREAS:	What do you look for then, Uncle?
LUCAS:	The beauty and harmony in God's heavenly design.
COPERNICUS:	That's what I try to see, too.
LUCAS:	Wonderful! Whenever the sky is clear, we'll look together.

CHORUS:

I:	Under the benevolent Uncle Lucas,
II:	Who provided for his sister's family,
III:	Were planted these virtues in Nicolaus:
IV:	Wonder and altruism and piety.

I:	High school proved an inspiration,
II:	For his teacher loved astronomy, too;
III:	Hours in joint observation
IV:	Helped Copernicus find what was true.

I:	On to Krakow University,
II:	He mastered math so complicated,
III:	And came to doubt the old certainty:
IV:	"Around the Earth everything rotated."

Scene II: Krakow University, Poland, c. 1494.

CELTES:	What's up, good friend? You have that anxious look again.
COPERNICUS:	Ptolemy's system makes me anxious! All my observations and calculations only cast doubt on its explanations.
CELTES:	It *is* rather complicated. But listen, let's go somewhere else. Doubting Ptolemy in public can be dangerous. We could end up the main course at the next church barbeque.
COPERNICUS:	You're always the wit! (*sighs*) There must be a clearer and more consistent system.
CELTES:	For explaining the movements of all heavenly bodies without Ptolemy's imaginary orbits?
COPERNICUS:	Precisely! My studies are pointing to a simple and harmonious model.
CELTES:	That's what my old professor was after.

COPERNICUS: What was his guiding idea?

CELTES: He was afraid to make it public.

COPERNICUS: The Earth moves...around the sun!

CELTES: Yes! It's so simple, yet profound!

COPERNICUS: It makes a yearly revolution around the sun...and... according to my observations, it moves about itself, a daily rotation on its axis.

CELTES: These are revolutionary ideas! Be careful how you communicate them, my dear friend.

COPERNICUS: Of course. I have no desire to draw attention to myself— only to my observations, my calculations. You can keep truth quiet, even for a long time. But you can never kill it.

CHORUS:

I: Uncertain of his life's direction,
II: He trekked to Renaissance Italy,
III: Hoping to find the right profession
IV: To set his spirit free.

I: Church administrator and physician
II: His studies prepared him to be,
III: And a well-muscled mathematician,
IV: For his knockout blow of Ptolemy.

I: But Italy was more than a training ground;
II: Friends like Michelangelo touched his soul.
III: Through them Copernicus forever found
IV: The inspiration to reach his goal.

I: His goal to bring health and harmony
II: To the sick, the feuding, the oppressed,
III: And to the world of astronomy,
IV: Putting muddled theories forever to rest.

20 Exciting Plays for Medieval History Classes

Scene III: Frauenburg, Poland, summer, 1540.

RHETICUS: How's Copernicus feeling today?

GIESE: Not well, I'm afraid.

RHETICUS: What ails him?

GIESE: Nothing in particular . . . just a deep and consuming wearinesss. He's working himself into the grave.

RHETICUS: And he's still the doctor all the peasants come to, day or night?

GIESE: He's the one, even now . . . and he never charges them a penny!

RHETICUS: But didn't you tell me the bishop keeps Copernicus constantly running about with menial tasks?

GIESE: Yes . . . because he hates the ideas of our friend. The bishop will do anything to humiliate, wear down, or discredit Copernicus.

RHETICUS: But doesn't the bishop insist that Copernicus remain his personal doctor?

GIESE: He does. When the bishop was gravely ill, who came to his rescue?

RHETICUS: But how could he treat so cruelly the one person who made him well? It doesn't make sense.

GIESE: Of course not . . . but the bishop has plenty of company.

RHETICUS: You mean all the so-called learned people who criticize Copernicus' ideas?

GIESE: More than scholarly criticism, my friend! They've even written and performed gross plays, mocking our friend and his astronomical ideas. They think by making him a buffoon on the stage, he can be ignored in scientific debate. There's your real nonsense!

RHETICUS: It's all so unjust. Copernicus is such a kind, generous, and peaceful man.

20 Exciting Plays for Medieval History Classes

GIESE:	That's for certain! But those virtues don't matter to pig-headed bullies! Why, years ago the Master of the Teutonic Knights and his goons came after Copernicus.
RHETICUS:	What happened? What did they want?
GIESE:	Those chain-mail brains thought they knew more about astronomy than Copernicus! They said it was their "duty" to stamp out these "Polish perversions."
RHETICUS:	Did they torture our friend?
GIESE:	No. It ended up that Copernicus knew more about siege defenses than they knew science! They were forced to retreat and lick their wounds.
RHETICUS:	I suppose there will always be people who will fight against new ideas.
GIESE:	Our friend has dealt with them all his life.
RHETICUS:	Then, why won't he publish his book? His ideas aren't a secret. People need to read all his research to fully appreciate his system.
GIESE:	I agree. But he's not eager to live through any more public controversies. When Protestants and Catholics fight, he grieves deeply.
RHETICUS:	I'm a Protestant and he's always treated me like a brother.
GIESE:	That's his nature. He's reluctant to publish because he doesn't want to see his followers fighting with Ptolemy's defenders.
RHETICUS:	Will he ever agree to publish?
GIESE:	Yes . . . when he thinks his earthly end is near.
RHETICUS:	How tragic! To think he'll never see his ideas vindicated, he'll never experience the respect and acclaim he deserves.
GIESE:	He's not concerned with such things. He's lived with his great truth most of his life, and for Copernicus, that's been satisfaction enough.

Epilogue

CHORUS:

I:	Bravery and brilliance graced the man,
II:	His life ever marked by goodness;
III:	He changed the world by his stand,
IV:	The Pole we call Copernicus.
I:	On his shoulders would stand giants—
II:	Galileo, Kepler, Newton, and Einstein, too;
III:	Those who changed the world of science,
IV:	And humanity's point of view.

Cortés and the Conquest of Mexico, 1518-1521

```
┌─────────────────────────────────────────────────────────────────┐
│                          Characters                               │
│                                                                   │
│   PRIEST, Aztec                    AGUILAR, conquistador           │
│   MOCTEZUMA, Aztec ruler             translator                   │
│     (often spelled Montezuma)      AIDE (to Moctezuma)             │
│   VELÁZQUEZ, Spanish official       DIAZ, conquistador writer      │
│   CORTÉS, conquistador leader      CHORUS I, II, III, IV           │
│   ALVARADO, conquistador                                          │
│                                                                   │
└─────────────────────────────────────────────────────────────────┘
```

Scene I: Royal palace, Tenochtitlan, Mexico, c. 1518.

PRIEST: One more bad omen, Moctezuma.

MOCTEZUMA: Another earthquake?

PRIEST: No. Our astronomers just observed a comet.

MOCTEZUMA: Soon we will be in a One Reed Year. Will this be the fateful one?

PRIEST: Meaning . . . ?

MOCTEZUMA: When the exiled god, Quetzalcoatl, returns from the east—

PRIEST: Now I understand. Our traditions say this god will return with white skin and a full beard.

MOCTEZUMA: And that he will be full of anger because we did not heed his call to end the human sacrifices.

PRIEST: How could we have obeyed him? Without feeding the gods warm human hearts, the earth, wind, sun, and rain would all die!

MOCTEZUMA: And our great civilization would be no more!

155   *20 Exciting Plays for Medieval History Classes*

PRIEST: What could we do if Quetzalcoatl did return? Fighting a god is very risky...and dangerous.

MOCTEZUMA: I know. Our only hope would be to bribe him with gifts to return to the east.

(Enter AIDE.)

AIDE: White men have landed on the Yucatán!

MOCTEZUMA: We must work harder to please the hungry gods!

Scene II: Governor's house, Santiago, Cuba, January, 1519.

VELÁZQUEZ: Cortés, before leaving here, I want you to be absolutely certain of your mission's objective.

CORTÉS: Yes, Governor.

VELÁZQUEZ: Now, Alvarado here has created quite a stir with his stories about his journey west.

CORTÉS: What can you expect? The men found a new land, rumored to be full of gold and silver.

VELÁZQUEZ: I'll tell you what I expect. I expect your expedition to always stay near the coast, and only be concerned with gathering facts—not chasing rumors of riches! Understood?

CORTÉS: Of course.

VELÁZQUEZ: Good. I'll expect your return in a few months. Otherwise, I'll send royal forces after you!

(He exits.)

ALVARADO: My, my, he wants to keep you on a very short leash.

CORTÉS: Which I'll cut as soon as we land.

ALVARADO: That could be risky.

CORTÉS: I was made to take risks. Do you think I'm the type who's content to make reports for some hogheaded, gutless, lazy official?

ALVARADO:	Well . . . what type *are* you?
CORTÉS:	A conqueror! One who returns with gold and glory, not just maps and facts.
ALVARADO:	And how do you expect to pull this off? You're only authorized to take 550 men.
CORTÉS:	Correct, but I've chosen only tough and skilled men who share my goal. We'll also bring horses.
ALVARADO:	You expect to conquer so much with so little? A great and powerful nation could await you.
CORTÉS:	Possibly . . . but I'm counting on the horses and guns to dazzle anyone who meets us.
ALVARADO:	You're a dreamer. That's not enough.
CORTÉS:	You forget—God is on our side. Will you join us?
ALVARADO:	Now you're being cynical.
CORTÉS:	I am not! I set off to conquer for God, glory, and . . . gold.
ALVARADO:	You *really* believe you'll succeed. Yes, I'll go.

Scene III: Tabasco, Yucatán, March, 1519.

CORTÉS:	Do you think the Tabascoans will continue fighting?
ALVARADO:	They are very brave. They stood their ground even against our cannons. But our horses. . . .
CORTÉS:	What a panic they caused!
ALVARADO:	They think they're something supernatural. The Tabascoans will sue for peace . . . soon, I'm quite certain.
CORTÉS:	Then we had better be ready for their envoys. Get Aguilar, since he seems to know their language.

Scene IV: Hours later.

AGUILAR: Commander Cortés, the Tabascoan lords wish to negotiate a peace.

CORTÉS: Excellent! Ask them to come here in two hours. I want to prepare a pleasant and dignified reception for them.

Scene V: Two hours later.

AGUILAR: Commander Cortés! Wonderful news! The Tabascoans have presented you a most precious peace offering.

CORTÉS: How much gold? Silver? Well?

AGUILAR: A woman!

CORTÉS: Aguilar! We didn't risk our lives for a—

AGUILAR: Actually, they are giving us twenty—but one speaks both Mayan and Aztec! I can speak Mayan with her! We talked about many things.

CORTÉS: What did she say about the Aztecs?

AGUILAR: They are very powerful. They have conquered many tribes, and these tribes hate them bitterly.

CORTÉS: Even now? Conquest is part of the natural order of things. The conquered should simply make the best of change.

AGUILAR: Oh? How would you make the best of ever-increasing taxes, and worse still, seeing your sons and daughters taken away—

CORTÉS: —as slaves. It's been going on for centuries.

AGUILAR: No! No! Even worse—to have their warm beating hearts carved out to feed the Aztec gods!

CORTÉS: I see. How many people have the Aztecs conquered?

AGUILAR: I'm not sure, but I know there are more than 370 towns of unwilling subjects.

CORTÉS:	Do you think they could be roused into a rebellion?
AGUILAR:	Only if they have some confidence of winning. Right now the Aztecs are too strong, their armies much larger and better organized.
CORTÉS:	Then we'll give these tribes the confidence of our cannons! If we're patient and prudent, we can build a great alliance against the Aztecs.
AGUILAR:	Many of these tribes speak the Aztec tongue. The woman will be most useful to us.
CORTÉS:	Yes, especially if she can read their leaders' intentions. What's her name?
AGUILAR:	I'm not sure.
CORTÉS:	Then let's really make her one of us. We'll have her baptized and called "Dona Marina." Now, let's get ready for the long journey inland.

Scene VI: Royal palace, Tenochtitlan, October, 1519.

AIDE:	Grave news from our spies: The white men are less than ten days journey away.
MOCTEZUMA:	All my gifts of goodwill when they landed would not persuade them to turn back.
AIDE:	The disks of hammered gold and silver, all the jewelry and textiles—it only made them greedy for more.
MOCTEZUMA:	What is their strength?
AIDE:	About five hundred white men.
MOCTEZUMA:	And they have made it this far? Why haven't the other tribes pushed them into the sea?
AIDE:	They have mighty animals, and powerful weapons that smoke. They do not fight to take prisoners as the tribes do.

PRIEST: Don't forget, their leader might be Quetzalcoatl... and men are no match for gods!

MOCTEZUMA: What are the conquered tribes doing?

AIDE: Many have made peace with the white men. Some are even joining them.

MOCTEZUMA: Tell me about these white men.

AIDE: They wear heavy metal armor. Everywhere they go they make the people stop the human sacrifices.

PRIEST: They must have a very aggressive religion.

AIDE: They are very determined. They have killed thousands, traveled two months up and down the mountains. They have suffered through cold, hunger, thirst, and evil weather. Yet, they keep coming, headed straight for our city.

MOCTEZUMA: How do they get the other tribes to join them?

AIDE: They have a very smart woman who speaks our tongue. She is very shrewd, and skilled in diplomacy.

PRIEST: What are you going to do?

MOCTEZUMA: What can I do? If their leader is Quetzalcoatl, killing him might be the end of us. I will meet with him, and try peacefully to persuade him to return to the east. Send my nephew to greet the white men at Ayotzingo, and then escort them into the capital.

Scene VII: Entering Tenochtitlan, November 8, 1519.

DIAZ: Pedro, are we dreaming?

ALVARADO: Never have I seen such a grand city!

DIAZ: Nothing in Spain can rival it.

ALVARADO: How could they build all of this... in the middle of a lake?

20 Exciting Plays for Medieval History Classes

DIAZ:	I have no idea. Tall buildings, long and wide causeways over the water....
ALVARADO:	Look! What an ingenious grid of canals and streets!
DIAZ:	What's that growing in the strips of land between the waters?
ALVARADO:	Maize. It's their staple crop.
DIAZ:	Amazing! What's Cortés planning after the big meeting with Moctezuma?
ALVARADO:	Stay here as a guest, study the Aztec defenses, and then make his move to take over.
DIAZ:	What? Here? In the middle of their capital, cut off from the mainland? How could Cortés conquer all this?
ALVARADO:	Dona Marina has learned that Moctezuma is paralyzed by a prophecy... that one day an important god will return from exile... and he will appear as a white man with a full beard!
DIAZ:	You mean, Moctezuma believes Cortés is a god?
ALVARADO:	Yes! He won't lift a finger against us.
DIAZ:	Maybe so, but I wonder how his people will react when Cortés makes his move.

Scene VIII: Royal palace, Tenochtitlan, April, 1520.

ALVARADO:	Governor Velázquez has sent a large force to capture you, and end your unauthorized conquest of Mexico.
CORTÉS:	Where are they now?
ALVARADO:	Cempoala. The report says they have many more men than we have. What are you going to do?
CORTÉS:	I will not be stopped! I have Moctezuma in the palm of my hand. We'll just have to pay a surprise visit to the governor's forces.

ALVARADO:	You mean...abandon Tenochtitlan?
CORTÉS:	No. We'll leave a sufficient force here to keep the Aztec leaders at bay. I want you in charge.
ALVARADO:	Thank you for your confidence in me. What do you plan on doing with the governor's forces? Slaughter them all?
CORTÉS:	No! Capture their leader and win the others over to our cause. We'll need them all, sooner or later.
ALVARADO:	Good luck! I won't let you down here.

Scene IX: Royal palace, Tenochtitlan, late June, 1520.

CORTÉS:	What has happened during my absence?
ALVARADO:	Things are very tense and unsettled. Moctezuma has lost power. The opposition is in control.
CORTÉS:	And they won't have any religious fears about attacking me. Alvarado! Don't you realize I've walked into a trap?
ALVARADO:	What should we do?
CORTÉS:	Get ready to fight our way out of the city! And if we survive, regroup with our Indian allies and prepare for the final battle for all Mexico.

Epilogue

CHORUS:

I:	The Aztecs revolted, even stoned their "king";
II:	The Spanish made a bloody retreat.
III:	Would this disaster serve to bring
IV:	The Europeans a lasting defeat?
I:	But Cortés escaped, and gathered allies—
II:	Tribes who fought with no pity;

20 Exciting Plays for Medieval History Classes

III:	Now the test: which culture survives?
IV:	Opened with the siege of Tenochtitlan City.
I:	The siege was long and full of fury,
II:	No quarter given by either side;
III:	On the water, and in the city,
IV:	Aztec power raged, then died.
I:	In its place emerged the Spaniard,
II:	With his culture deep and wide;
III:	Unto Cortés all Mexico deferred,
IV:	But never surrendered its native pride.

Elizabeth I
(1533–1603)

Characters

ALFRED, royal messenger   **ELIZABETH**, queen of England
LADY BRYAN, governess   **GALLY** and **OPPIE**, royal coast
CHORUS I, II, III, IV   watchers
CECIL, Elizabeth's chief adviser   **LEICESTER**, Elizabeth's confidant

---

Scene I: Royal household, London, England, May 19, 1536.

ALFRED: I bring grave news from Tower Green. Anne Boleyn is dead.

LADY BRYAN: Did she suffer?

ALFRED: No. King Henry brought over an expert from France. He used a sword instead of an ax.

LADY BRYAN: My . . . how thoughtful of husband Henry.

ALFRED: Are you going to tell Anne Boleyn's daughter?

LADY BRYAN: Elizabeth? Of course not! She's not even three.

ALFRED: What will happen to her now?

LADY BRYAN: I'll look after her. But remember, she's lost her father as well.

ALFRED: What do you mean? The king's as healthy as a young stag. Why, he's out hunting this very afternoon in Richmond Park.

LADY BRYAN: Out hunting for Jane Seymour, you mean.

ALFRED: She's very beautiful . . . and Henry's determined to sire a son. I'm told the two will wed tomorrow.

LADY BRYAN: Don't you understand? When Henry lost interest in Anne Boleyn, he forgot about his daughter Elizabeth as well.

ALFRED: I suppose if Henry does produce a male heir, England will forget about Elizabeth, too.

LADY BRYAN: Not very likely. She's very bright and spirited. She'll make her mark someday.

CHORUS:

I:	England was filled with turmoil and strife,
II:	Uncertainty ruled the day;
III:	Who would be the king's next wife,
IV:	And how would he make her pay?
I:	Jane Seymour paid her historic debt
II:	With her life, giving birth to a son;
III:	Elizabeth remained a figure of neglect
IV:	As Henry pursued his debaucheries of fun.
I:	But a life of excess took its toll—
II:	At fifty-six his reign was ended;
III:	A new name topped the royal roll
IV:	When Edward the Sixth, his son, ascended.
I:	But the teenage monarch soon after died,
II:	And Henry's first daughter entered the scene;
III:	Provoking and pulling to the Catholic side,
IV:	Mary tormented England as the "bloody queen."
I:	In the year fifteen and fifty-eight,
II:	England was poor and downcast;
III:	Vitality sapped by leeches of hate,
IV:	Protestants and Catholics holding fast.

20 Exciting Plays for Medieval History Classes

I:	Holding fast, dividing a nation,
II:	A grim fate was held in store;
III:	Before each English man and woman,
IV:	The endless abyss of civil war.

I:	But in that year died Queen Mary,
II:	And was born a new chapter and age;
III:	Destiny called Elizabeth to carry
IV:	England across its golden page.

I:	What kind of person, the new queen?
II:	She fancied dancing, yet did manage
III:	Fast horses, and men of minds so keen
IV:	In Latin or a Romance language.

I:	Though raised in the Protestant creed,
II:	She early embraced toleration,
III:	Sensing England's paramount need
IV:	For peace and order through moderation.

I:	Her strength was not born from beauty,
II:	But a will steeled hard in life's fire,
III:	And devotion, beyond noble duty,
IV:	To all England—her steadfast desire.

Scene II: Queen's chambers, London, January, 1559.

CECIL:	All preparations for your coronation are completed.
ELIZABETH:	Very good. But I have more serious affairs to discuss with you.
CECIL:	I am at your service.
ELIZABETH:	And what does *that* mean?

20 Exciting Plays for Medieval History Classes

CECIL:	To carry out the desires of my queen.
ELIZABETH:	What about *your* desires, *your* aims... apart from me, William Cecil?
CECIL:	Why, to serve England. What are you really seeking?
ELIZABETH:	Someone as close to me as the clothes I wear who will not be corrupted. An adviser who does not seek personal wealth or power... one who will always be loyal and true to me, and to England. Are you that man?
CECIL:	I am.
ELIZABETH:	I know. Now, let us begin this reign. What are the most pressing problems facing England?
CECIL:	Foremost is the religious situation. The pressures within the country, and from abroad, to make us all Catholic again are tremendous. Civil war or invasion are likely if something isn't done.
ELIZABETH:	I was raised a Protestant, but my policy—England's policy—will be to throw the waters of moderation on all fires of fanaticism.
CECIL:	And the role of the Church of England, your father's creation?
ELIZABETH:	To be a church that unites England. Catholics must be treated gently, and respected as English.
CECIL:	I see. A second major problem involves our relations with other countries. England desperately needs a long period of peace. But that will be most difficult to accomplish.
ELIZABETH:	Not if we avoid entangling alliances.
CECIL:	And how can that be done? Half of Europe wants to murder you.
ELIZABETH:	Or marry me... once I wed, England will be tied to another country. But if I keep all suitors waiting and hoping for my hand, England will be given years of peace.
CECIL:	A virgin queen... it may work... for a while....

20 Exciting Plays for Medieval History Classes

ELIZABETH:	It will! What king or prince would attack us if he is seeking me as a royal bride? Our trade and commerce must have a long peace!
CECIL:	You've anticipated my last point: England's economy is a wreck.
ELIZABETH:	Because the value of our money is uncertain. Right?
CECIL:	Right. Our trade and industry will never flourish without a sound and stable currency.
ELIZABETH:	And neither will this government! Our forts and navy must be rebuilt. We cannot afford such expenditures without a strong and growing economy.
CECIL:	You are most perceptive. We agree on what England most needs at this time.
ELIZABETH:	Yes, but you forgot one important item—the spirit of our people.
CECIL:	What exactly do you mean?
ELIZABETH:	Today, England is like a great bird that is young and wounded. We have discussed how the healing must first take place, with patience, discipline, and wisdom.
CECIL:	Yes.
ELIZABETH:	But let us never forget that a great bird was made to fly— boldly, proudly, and in great freedom.
CECIL:	To the ends of the earth!
ELIZABETH:	Yes! I want my reign to see England soar, soar above all others in trade, art, and science.
CECIL:	An England all can be proud of!

CHORUS:

I:	Peace was bought, with delicacy and tact,
II:	The currency made strong and sound;
III:	A vigorous economy became a fact,
IV:	And the chains of despair steadily unbound.

     20 Exciting Plays for Medieval History Classes

I:	She attracted the best and the brightest
II:	To run the ship of state,
III:	Steering a course thought wisest:
IV:	Make England sole master of its fate.

I:	But the Catholic threat would not die,
II:	For Mary, Queen of Scots, ever schemed
III:	To bring down Elizabeth, by and by,
IV:	And with Philip's Spain she treacherously teamed.

I:	But Elizabeth would not be shaken,
II:	And Mary alone lost her head;
III:	The dreams of the Armada did waken
IV:	To England's new power instead.

Scene III: Lizard Head, England, 3:00 P.M., July 19, 1588.

GALLY:	Do you really think old Philip will send his armada?
OPPIE:	And why has Her Majesty sent us out here to scan the sea? Certainly not to whale watch. Of course the Armada's coming!
GALLY:	But I thought Drake burned a lot of their ships about a year ago.
OPPIE:	He certainly did! Drake's been giving the Spanish fits for years, all over the world.
GALLY:	Yeah...remember in 1580 when he sailed the *Golden Hind* into Plymouth?
OPPIE:	She was carrying so much Spanish silver and gold, it's a wonder she didn't sink.
GALLY:	We couldn't believe it...that old pirate got away from the Spanish by sailing around the world!
OPPIE:	The queen gave him quite a nice reception, too, for his efforts.

20 Exciting Plays for Medieval History Classes

GALLY:	That she did, and made the Spanish madder than a hungry dog that's had his bone robbed. But tell me, how'd old Drake escape from the Spanish and then later sneak into their port and burn half their navy?
OPPIE:	Gally, my friend, you are a bit thick above the neck! He had faster, lighter, and more maneuverable ships. Spanish ships are all fat, slow, and high-riding.
GALLY:	But they have big guns and can carry a lot of troops.
OPPIE:	True enough.
GALLY:	Then, if they do come, do we have a chance? And won't English Catholics help the Spanish?
OPPIE:	I'm confident our ships will prevail. And don't worry about traitors. English Catholics will fight for England! The lord high admiral himself is a Catholic.
GALLY:	Ho! There's the Armada! Light the first warning bonfire!
OPPIE:	Now the world will see what the English are made of.

Scene IV: Leicester's headquarters, Tilbury, England, August 10.

ELIZABETH:	Why haven't we heard any news?
LEICESTER:	The sea battles are raging over a large area. It will take some time before we get an accurate picture.
	(Enter messenger, who gives Elizabeth a note.)
ELIZABETH:	Oh no! The invasion force is crossing the Channel this very minute! I must speak to the troops!
LEICESTER:	You can't do that...it's much too dangerous!
ELIZABETH:	Dangerous? How can you say such a thing when England's sons will soon face death! I must speak to my troops!
LEICESTER:	Very well, but you must carry this helmet and wear this steel corset.

20 Exciting Plays for Medieval History Classes

Scene V: At the front.

ELIZABETH: Men of England, as your queen I may have a weak and frail body, but my heart and guts are those of a lion! How dare any foreign power think to invade our blessed land. How dare anyone ever think our great people can be conquered. Never! Never! Never!

(Troops cheer.)

Scene VI: Hours later.

LEICESTER: My queen! The Spanish Armada is defeated! Remnants are retreating around Scotland and Ireland for Spain. There will be no invasion!

ELIZABETH: What blessed news! England is now free to pursue her destiny.

Legacy

CHORUS:

I:	With Spain defeated, England moved straight
II:	To the center of the world's stage,
III:	In a role destined as glorious and great,
IV:	Known as the Elizabethan Age.
I:	An age of poets, and ambitious desire,
II:	When England shifted into high gear,
III:	And daring seamen launched a global empire,
IV:	While the home soil grew William Shakespeare.
I:	A culture rooted, deep, worldwide,
II:	Praised, though sometimes cursed;
III:	The legacy of England's beloved bride,
IV:	Queen Elizabeth the First.

20 Exciting Plays for Medieval History Classes